BRAIN GAMES®

10·MINUTE
LARGE PRINT

WORD
PUZZLES

Publications International, Ltd.

Cover Puzzle: Wayne Robert Williams

Puzzle constructors: Cihan Altay, Chris Bolton, George Bredehorn, Myles Callum, Philip Carter, Jeff Cockrell, Don Cook, Mark Danna, Josie Faulkner, Erich Friedman, Grabarchuk Family, Luke Haward, Marilynn Huret, David Millar, Dan Moore, Michael Moreci, Alan Olschwang, Ellen F. Pill, Ph.D., Jamee Rotunno, Stephen Ryder, Pete Sarjeant, Paul Seaburn, Fraser Simpson, Startdl Puzzles, Terry Stickels, Wayne Robert Williams

Illustrators: Helem An, Chris Gattorna, Elizabeth Gerber, Robin Humer, Jen Torche

Louis Weber, CEO
Publications International, Ltd.
7373 North Cicero Avenue
Lincolnwood, Illinois 60712

ISBN: 978-1-4508-8797-7

Manufactured in U.S.A.

8 7 6 5 4 3 2 1

PUZZLE YOUR BRAIN, NOT YOUR EYES

You're holding the perfect pick-me-up for those moments of the day when it's time to step back and recharge. *Word Puzzles* is bursting with a variety of tricky and engaging word games that will challenge your language skills and keep you at the top of your game. These puzzles may leave you scratching your head, but they won't leave you squinting. Each puzzle is printed in readable type so you can work your mental muscle while letting your eyes rest.

We've included an assortment of puzzles to get your wordy wit flowing, from anagrams and addagrams to word jigsaws and ladders, and plenty in between. You'll have fun with the familiar favorites and discover absorbing new variations along the way.

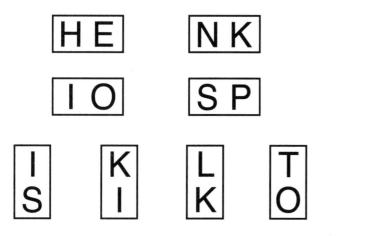 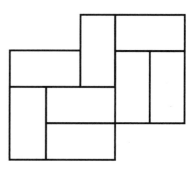

These word puzzles aren't just for fun, though. Scientists have shown that exercising the brain by working puzzles can increase your brain's flexibility, or neuroplasticity, keeping it supple and helping fend off the mental decline that often happens as people age. Research has even shown that those who engage in regular mental activities as part of their education or jobs are less likely to develop dementia.

The complex cognitive functions required to complete a puzzle involve a whole network of brain regions that work together to find the solution. You'll need to focus your attention and sharpen your vocabulary, planning, and problem-solving skills. And all of this comes with the pure pleasure you get from finding just the right words and letters to solve the puzzles.

Just as it's important to put in time at the gym to keep your body's health, it's also important to put in time with puzzles and other activities to keep your mind sharp. The portability of this book will help you put your money where your mouth is—since you can do them anywhere, there's no reason not to indulge in an enjoyable mental workout every day!

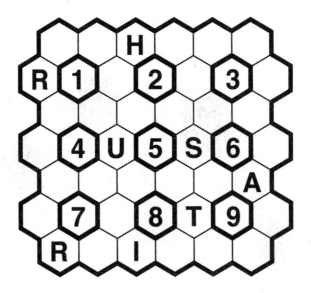

FITTING WORDS

In this miniature crossword, the clues are listed randomly and are numbered for convenience only. It is up to you to figure out the placement of the 9 answers. To help you, we've inserted one letter in the grid, and this is the only occurrence of that letter in the completed puzzle.

1. Always
2. Tusk material   IVORY
3. Street fighter's "duke"   FIST
4. Sandwich breads   RYES
5. Oliver Twist's request   FOOD
6. Worsted fabric   SERGE
7. Longest human bone   TIBIA
8. Arboretum's contents   TREES
9. Hankering   URGE

F	E	M	H	R
I	V	O	R	**Y**
S	E	R	EG	E
T	R	E	E	sS

Answers on page 172.

RHYME TIME

Each clue leads to a 2-word answer that rhymes, such as BIG PIG or STABLE TABLE. The numbers in parentheses after the clue give the number of letters in each word. For example, "cookware taken from the oven (3, 3)" would be "hot pot."

1. Less-optimistic orator (7, 7):

   _____ SPEAKER

2. Unhappy diploma recipient (3, 4):

   _____ _____

3. Pale-red cocktail (4, 5):

   PINK _____

4. Enormous marine mammal of fragile health (5, 5):

   _____ _____

5. What formaldehyde and fluoride do (5, 5):

   _____ _____

6. Tiny pears, apples, or bananas (6, 5):

   MINI _____

7. Hypothesis with a bright outlook (6, 6):

   _____ _____

8. Song for a barroom piano (6, 4):

   _____ _____

ADDAGRAM

This puzzle functions exactly like an anagram with an added step: In addition to being scrambled, each word below is missing the same letter. Discover the missing letter, then unscramble the words. When you do, you'll reveal a big cat, a liquid filter, a sharp-dressed man, and a watery weapon.

ORDEAL *leopard*   ᴾROOTED

ᴾDRAPE *dapper*   ᴾRELOCATE

WORD JIGSAW

Fit the pieces into the frame to form common words reading across and down. There's no need to rotate the pieces; they'll fit as shown, with each piece used exactly once.

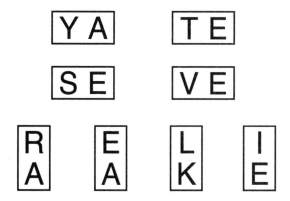
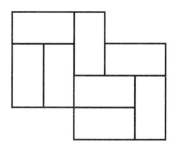

Answers on page 172.

2 BY 2

Rearrange the pairs of letters on the left to form the titles of famous books. Then match each title with one of the authors listed on the right.

For example: WS JA is Jaws and would match up with Peter Benchley on the right

1. TH EI ER GH WU TS IN GH   a) John Steinbeck

2. AN RI WI LE PV NK   b) Theodore Dreiser

3. WI TH LI TH ER FE FA   c) Charles Dickens

4. TI EO ES FT CI AL AT WO   d) George Orwell

THE GODFATHER
5. EG TH ER TH OD FA (G)   e) Dr. Seuss

6. RM AL AN IM FA   f) Emily Brontë

7. ER SI RR ST CA IE   g) Mario Puzo

8. US BI ON CR RO NS OE   h) Clarence Day

9. YR NN ER OW CA   i) Washington Irving

THE CAT IN THE HAT
10. AT TH TH AT EC IN EH (e)   j) Daniel Defoe

ANALOGIES

Study the relationships of the word pairs to discover what's missing.

1. Feather is to _____ as fur is to hide.

    A. pillow

    B. wing

    C. light

2. Card is to deck as _____ is to alphabet.

    A. letter

    B. language

    C. word

3. Ant is to colony as lion is to _____.

    A. safari

    B. cat

    C. pride

4. Pillow is to bed as _____ is to chair.

    A. cushion

    B. soft

    C. fluffy

     Answers on page 172.

ELEVATOR WORDS

Like an elevator, words move up and down the "floors" of this puzzle. Starting with the first answer, the second part of each answer carries down to become the first part of the following answer. With the clues given, complete the puzzle.

1. Case in _____   1. Example

2. _____ _____   2. Blunt

3. _____ _____   3. Empty place

4. _____ _____   4. Mir, e.g.

5. _____ _____   5. Pause in a broadcast

6. _____ _____   6. Acrobatics, in a way

7. _____ Queen   7. ABBA hit

Answers on page 172.   **10**

SPLIT DECISIONS

Fill in each set of empty cells with letters that will create English words reading both across and down. Letters may repeat within a single set. We've completed one set to get you started.

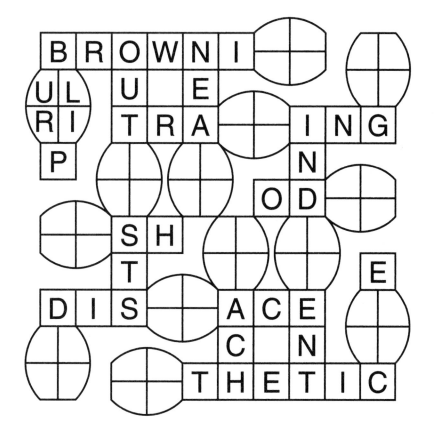

Answers on page 172.

ALPHABET SOUP

In this bowl of soup, there is at least one alphabet set (A to Z) swirling around. There are some extra letters given as well. Find the extra letters and unscramble them to reveal a girl's name name. Some letters have already been given.

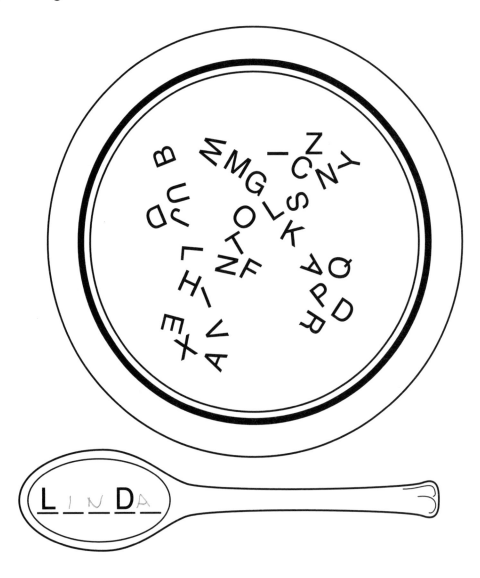

STRIKE UP THE BAND

Use the clues to change just one letter on each line to go from the top word to the bottom word. Do not change the order of the letters. You must have a common English word at each step.

DRUM

_____ African palm tree

__DORM__ building where a number of people sleep

_____ small, soft-bodied animal

_____ used

HORN

ADDAGRAM

This puzzle functions exactly like an anagram with an added step: In addition to being scrambled, each word or phrase below is missing the same letter. Discover the missing letter, then unscramble the words. When you do, you'll reveal 4 girls' names.

AXLES   NOMADS

SEA BALL   THE BLAZE

    Answers on page 172.

TANGLED WORDS

Think of this puzzle like a word search, only in reverse. Rather than finding the words in the grid, your job is to fill them in. Words begin only from the letters given in the shaded boxes and they appear in a straight line horizontally, vertically, or diagonally. They may appear forward or backward. When complete, every word will have been used, and the grid will have no empty squares.

ADRIANA	GAYLE	MATILDA
AMANDA	HEDY	MEDEA
AMBER	HEIDI	MELINDA
ANGELA	HILARY	MYRA
BARBARA	IRENE	NINA
CANDY	LARA	ROSA
CATHERINE	LAURA	ROSE
DEEDEE	MADELYN	RUBY
DIANE	MAMIE	SELMA
EDNA	MARLEE	TANYA
ELSA	MARTINA	THELMA
EMMA	MARY	

Answers on page 173.

ANSWER THE HOMOPHONE

You are given 2 words. Your objective is to come up with a set of homophones that would either precede or follow each of these words. For example, "guitar" and "second" would be "bass" and "base."

humor, whiskey

WORD SQUARE

Complete the word square below using 4 words that mean, in this order: get ready for, big, a jungle cat, and the back of a ship.

S	A	L	T	S
A				
L				
T				
S				

SWEETNESS

What 2 words that are different arrangements of the same 7 letters can be used to complete the sentence below?

Bears running back Walter Payton was so smooth and classy that he would never have celebrated a touchdown by _____ the _____ into the ground like many a showboating scorer in today's modern game.

WORD JIGSAW

Fit the pieces into the frame to form common words reading across and down. There's no need to rotate the pieces; they'll fit as shown, with each piece used once.

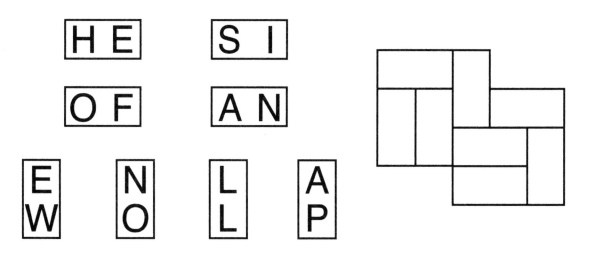

Answers on page 173.

CRYPTOKU

Answer the clues below to fill in the grid and discover the 6 different letters used in each 3 by 2 box. Just like a standard crossword, answers read across and down; numbers in parenthesis indicate how many letters are in the solution. And, like a code-doku, each letter appears only once in each 3 by 2 box. When complete, the shaded squares will reveal a mystery word.

ACROSS

1. Decay (3)

2. Rocky hilltop (3)

3. Expire (3)

DOWN

4. Period (3)

5. Anger (3)

5. Cravat (3)

DROP-A-LETTER

Only 5 of the letters in the top line will make their way through to the bottom of this maze and land in the squares below. Once they're there, the letters will spell out the answer to this riddle:

What 5-letter word is most often pronounced wrong?

Answer on page 173.

ELEVATOR WORDS

Like an elevator, words move up and down the "floors" of this puzzle. Starting with the first answer, the second part of each answer carries down to become the first part of the following answer. With the clues given, complete the puzzle.

1. Great _____   1. Montana city

2. _____ _____   2. Retreats

3. _____ _____   3. Remote rural area

4. _____ _____   4. US is 1; UK is 44

5. _____ _____   5. Euphemism

6. _____ _____   6. Microsoft Word
                               eclipsed it

7. _____ storm   7. 2000 George Clooney
                               film, with "The"

Answers on page 173.   **20**

FITTING WORDS

In this miniature crossword, the clues are listed randomly and are numbered for convenience only. It is up to you to figure out the placement of the 9 answers. To help you, we've inserted one letter in the grid, and this is the only occurrence of that letter in the completed puzzle.

1. Closed hand

2. Wife of Zeus

3. Double _____
   (DNA shape)

4. Takes no food

5. Kitchen's head honcho

6. Rub the wrong way

7. Alimony recipients

8. "Woe is me!"

9. Clear the chalkboard

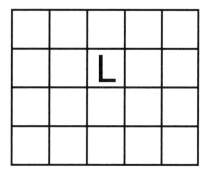

Answers on page 174.

SPELLEPHONE

In some areas of the United States, you can find out the time by picking up the phone and dialing N-E-R-V-O-U-S (637-8687). In the same way, the 8 phone numbers below can be translated into the names of 8 states. What are they?

A. 252-2262 _____

B. 356-7432 _____

C. 436-7442 _____

D. 463-4262 _____

E. 666-8262 _____

F. 639-9675 _____

G. 837-6668 _____

H. 996-6464 _____

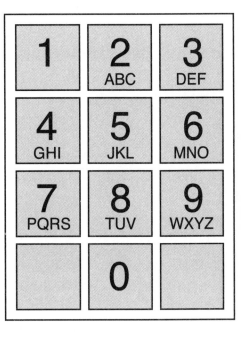

Answers on page 174.   **22**

ADDAGRAM

This puzzle functions exactly like an anagram with an added step: In addition to being scrambled, each word or phrase below is missing the same letter. Discover the missing letter, then unscramble the words. When you do, you'll reveal 4 common flowers.

CHOIR   LAID OFF

ONLINE AD   LINE HIM UP

WORD JIGSAW

Fit the pieces into the frame to form common words reading across and down. There's no need to rotate the pieces; they'll fit as shown, with each piece used once.

Answers on page 174.

ANAGRAMS FOREVER

What 2 words, formed from different arrangements of the same 8 letters, can be used to complete the sentence below?

Watching the long and boring miniseries in its _____ seemed liked an _____.

CROSSED WORDS

Unscramble the words in each line to solve the puzzle. The words cross on a letter that they share.

Clue: To go beyond, and to remain within.

```
        N
        E
        S
        D
        A
        E
        R
N M E A N T I M
        T
        N
        T
        C
```

DOUBLE JUMBLE

It's 2 jumbles in one! First, unscramble the 7 letters under each row of squares to form common English words. When you've done this, unscramble the letters running down each column in the blackened boxes to reveal 2 more related words.

WHUFISL

BIXTACA

BRAHBUR

CANORIA

SPELECI

Answers on page 174.

RHYME TIME

Each clue leads to a 2-word answer that rhymes, such as BIG PIG or STABLE TABLE. The numbers in parentheses after the clue give the number of letters in each word.

1. Cloistered man grew tiny (4, 6): _____ _____

2. Space telescope difficulty (6, 7): _____ _____

3. Shortness in duration of light humor (6, 7):

_____ _____

RIDDLE IN THE MIDDLE

Use the clues to complete the 5-letter answers, starting at the top and working your way down. When finished, read the letters in the squares with thick borders, from top to bottom, to reveal the answer to the riddle below.

What can only be filled or emptied by hand?

1. Start

2. Measuring stick

3. By yourself

4. Lid

5. Girl's outfit

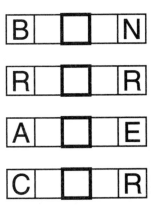

LANGUAGE DETECTIVE

There should be 6 words here, but the third word is missing. What should that word be? The words are connected in some way. You can figure it out by looking at the words carefully.

PERHAPS

BANANAS

———————

ETERNAL

LEGENDS

BRAIDED

Which of these is the missing word?

SNORKEL

ESQUIRE

TABASCO

KARAOKE

NATURAL

Answers on page 174.

CROSSED WORDS

Unscramble the words in each line to solve the puzzle. The words cross on a letter that they share.

Clue: Social evolution

```
            I
            E
            M
            V
D Z C E L   I   I I V
            P
            I
            T
            R
```

NUMBERS IN WORDS

Each of the 6 words below contains the name of a number. The numbers may read either forward or backward.

1. Existing

2. Freighters

3. Interplanetary

4. Meningitis

5. Lightwood

6. Phenomenal

ANALOGIES

Study the relationships of the word pairs to discover what's missing.

1. _____ is to India as Dutch is to Belgium.

    A. alphabet

    B. Hindi

    C. Flemish

2. Deer is to dear as pigeon is to _____.

    A. coop

    B. fly

    C. pidgin

3. Desert is to rainforest as _____ is to fastidious.

    A. negligent

    B. dry

    C. particular

4. Microscope is to _____ as stethoscope is to doctor.

    A. slide

    B. bacteriologist

    C. mechanic

Answers on page 175.

SPACE SAVERS

Two well-known proverbs are given below. No letter has been printed more than once in either of them, even if it appears in the proverb a number of times. For example: "RISEANDH" would be "RISE AND SHINE." Supply the missing letters and read the proverbs.

L O K B E F R Y U A P

W A S T E N O

ADD-A-WORD

Add one word to each of the 3-word sets to create new words or phrases. For example: In a set including "smith," "fore," and "game," the added word would be "word" (creating "wordsmith," "foreword," and "word game").

1. bed, salt, bottom: _____

2. bike, pay, track: _____

3. quick, trap, box: _____

4. flag, tomb, wall: _____

5. back, play, hog: _____

6. rare, worm, bound: _____

Answers on page 175.

SPLIT DECISIONS

Fill in each set of empty cells with letters that will create English words reading both across and down. Letters may repeat within a single set. We've completed one set to get you started.

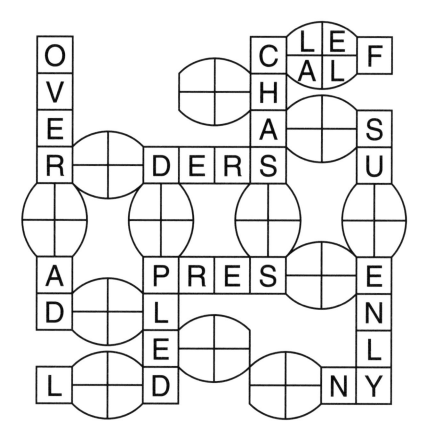

Answers on page 175.

NAME CALLING

Decipher the encoded words in the quips below using the numbers and letters on the phone pad. Remember that each number can stand for any of three or four possible letters.

1. A virtuoso is a musician with very high 6-6-7-2-5 standards. _____

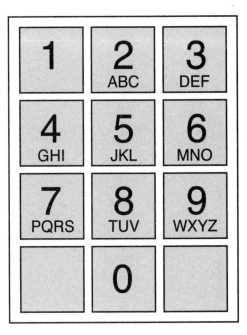

2. 8-4-7-8-8-3 is its own punishment. _____

3. The 4-4-7-2-3-3-3 is the highest form of animal life. _____

4. Help Wanted: Dynamite Factory. Must be willing to 8-7-2-8-3-5. _____

5. Remember, paper is always 7-8-7-6-6-4-3-7 at the perforations. _____

Answers on page 175.

WORD JIGSAW

Fit the pieces into the frame to form common words reading across and down. There's no need to rotate the pieces; they'll fit as shown, with each piece used once.

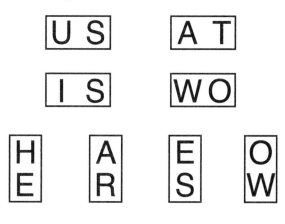

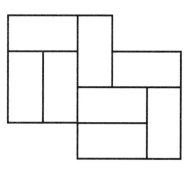

WORD LADDER

Use the clues to change just one letter on each line to go from the top word to the bottom word. Do not change the order of the letters. You must have a common English word at each step.

DRONE

_____ a herd of livestock

_____ full of treasure

_____ to find sufficient evidence

_____ liable to prostrations

PRUNE

Answers on page 175.

CRY, BABY

Not into action films or spy movies? How about a good tearjerker? Just rearrange the letters so you'll know what to rent. And don't forget the tissues, you'll need 'em!

1. INNERTUBE FORCE _____

2. DOLLY LEER _____

3. GRAIN SNOBS _____

4. CIA TINT _____

5. SO OVERTLY _____

OPPOSITES

Use the letters below to fill in the boxes and reveal the 2 related words. Connected boxes share the same letter.

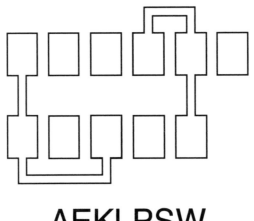

AEKLPSW

FINDING YOU

Ignoring spaces and punctuation, underline all 12 occurrences of the consecutive letters Y-O-U in the paragraph below.

Young Yoda found a yo-yo under your Christmas tree. He tried to use it, but he looked like a monkey out of his tree. After hitting his head, he called his youthful friend Yoric and said, "Hurry, ouch!" Yoric rode the Tokyo Underground all the way to Youngstown, whistling the ditty "O Ulysses." "You're in luck, Yoda," said Yoric, "I'm a yo-yo user, too." Yoric taught Yoda to yo-yo, and in appreciation Yoda took some candy out and gave it to his friend.

Answers on page 176.

ELEVATOR WORDS

Like an elevator, words move up and down the "floors" of this puzzle. Starting with the first answer, the second part of each answer carries down to become the first part of the following answer. With the clues given, complete the puzzle.

1. Squawk _____

2. _____ _____

3. _____ _____

4. _____ _____

5. _____ _____

6. _____ _____

7. _____ sitter

1. Intercom speaker

2. Slow-moving pet

3. Type of sweater

4. Piece of equipment for an ice hockey player

5. Highway protection

6. Boundary made of split logs

7. One who is undecided

Answers on page 176. **36**

ANAGRAM SENTENCES

What 2 words, formed from different arrangements of the same 3 letters, can be used to complete the sentences below?

1. There were no seats left so she sat on the _____ of her best _____.

2. Her _____ could _____ up a dozen numbers in his head.

3. The beauty queen _____ hair that is _____ blond.

4. Her husband _____ her son are both named _____.

5. For lunch she drank a cup of _____ and _____ a tuna fish sandwich.

Answers on page 176.

FITTING WORDS

In this miniature crossword, the clues are listed randomly and are numbered for convenience only. It is up to you to figure out the placement of the 9 answers. To help you, we've inserted one letter in the grid, and this is the only occurrence of that letter in the completed puzzle.

1. Howls at the moon

2. Catch sight of

3. Licorice flavoring

4. _____ monster (lizard)

5. Kennel cries

6. From scratch

7. Roll with lox

8. Moves to and fro

9. Minus

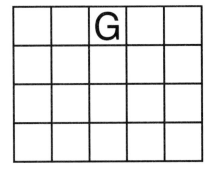

ADDAGRAM

This puzzle functions exactly like an anagram with an added step: In addition to being scrambled, each word or phrase below is missing the same letter. Discover the missing letter, then unscramble the words. When you do, you'll reveal 4 astrological signs.

CRANE   SPIES

IS POOR   RAIN CROP

WORD JIGSAW

Fit the pieces into the frame to form common words reading across and down. There's no need to rotate the pieces; they'll fit as shown, with each piece used once.

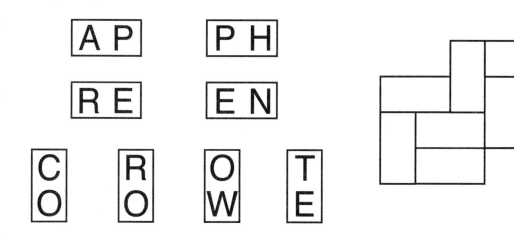

Answers on page 176.

CHAIN WORDS

Place 3 letters in the middle squares that will complete one word and start another. For example, TAR would complete GUI - TAR - GET.

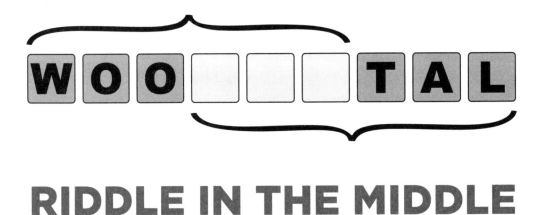

RIDDLE IN THE MIDDLE

Use the clues to complete the 5-letter answers, starting at the top and working your way down. When finished, read the letters in the squares with thick borders, from top to bottom, to reveal the answer to the riddle below.

What word becomes shorter when lengthened?

1. Squander
2. Bridal party member
3. Squat down
4. Ahead of time
5. Private teacher

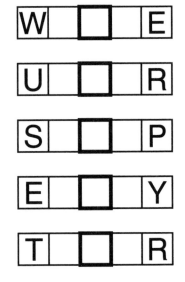

Answers on page 176.

DIY CROSSWORD

Fit the given words into the crossword grid. Be careful with your selections though—more words are provided than are needed.

BEEN

CAT

CRATE

ION

RUN

SCAR

SEE

SUR

TAB

TO

TRAIN

UR

Answers on page 177.

HONEYCOMB CROSSWORD

Answer each clue with a 6-letter word. Write the words in a clockwise direction around the numerals in the grid. Words overlap each other and may start in any of the spaces around the numerals. We've placed some letters to get you started.

1. Inform

2. Hardly ever

3. Place inside

4. Like a citrus fruit

5. Frivolity

6. Creates cloth

7. Take a trip

8. Tasty morsel

9. Virgil's epic poem

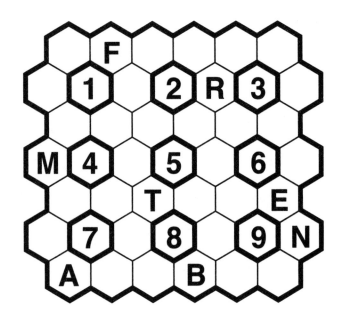

Answers on page 177.

CHAIN WORDS

Place 3 letters in the middle squares that will complete one word and start another. For example, TAR would complete GUI - TAR - GET.

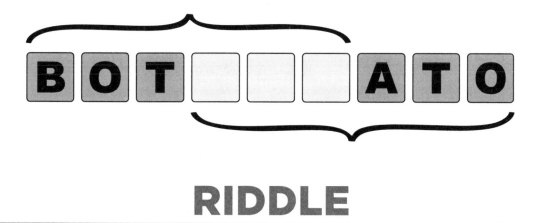

RIDDLE

Little Jimmy goes to his grandmother's home after a day's work on the farm during his summer vacation. "So what did you do today on the farm Jimmy?" asked his grandmother. "I have been producing grass mowed and cured for use as fodder during the time that the luminous orb, the light of which constitutes day, emits radiance," replied Little Jimmy.

"Oh, I see," said his grandmother. "I can tell you enjoyed doing that."

What had Little Jimmy been doing?

Answers on page 177.

WORD COLUMNS

Find the hidden phrase by using the letters directly below each of the blank squares. Each letter is used only once. A black square or the end of the line indicates the end of a word.

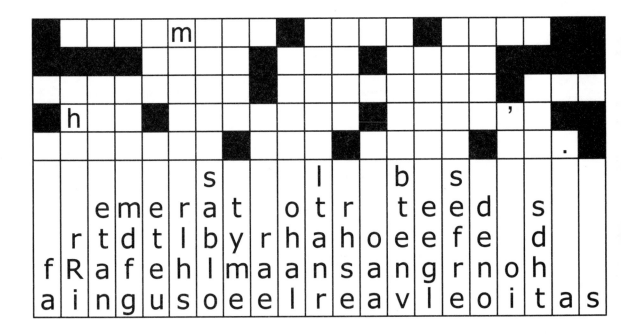

WORD LADDER

Use the clues to change just one letter on each line to go from the top word to the bottom word. Do not change the order of the letters. You must have a common English word at each step.

SISTER

_____ looks after house or baby

_____ not sweet

_____ wounded by teeth

KITTEN

ANAGRAM SENTENCES

What 2 words, formed from different arrangements of the same 3 letters, can be used to complete the sentences below?

1. She smeared black _____ on a canvas and called it _____.

2. If you have _____ doubts, vote _____.

3. Changing times _____ the sign of the end of an _____.

Answers on page 177.

ELEVATOR WORDS

Like an elevator, words move up and down the "floors" of this puzzle. Starting with the first answer, the second part of each answer carries down to become the first part of the following answer. With the clues given, complete the puzzle.

1. Almond _____   1. Marzipan cousin

2. _____ _____   2. It's made to look like the real thing

3. _____ _____   3. Place for diamonds

4. _____ _____   4. Like some sales

5. _____ _____   5. Like some TVs

6. _____ _____   6. Something many an actress has

7. _____ dropper   7. One who pretends to know celebs

Answers on page 177.   **46**

WEDGEWORDS

Fit the words into the grid reading across and down. One word will appear twice. Two letters have already been given.

AISLE INKER INLET

PEERS RESTS RISKS

STAIR STRIP TWINE

  Answers on page 177.

SAY WHAT?

Below is a group of words that, when properly arranged in the blanks, reveal a quote from Bela Lugosi.

personally never might vampire don't

"I have _____ met a _____ _____,

but I _____ know what _____ happen

tomorrow."

WORD TRIANGLE

Spell a 10-letter word by moving between adjacent letters. Every letter will be used at least once, but no letter will be used consecutively. Begin at any letter.

SPLIT DECISIONS

Fill in each set of empty cells with letters that will create English words reading both across and down. Letters may repeat within a single set. We've completed one set to get you started.

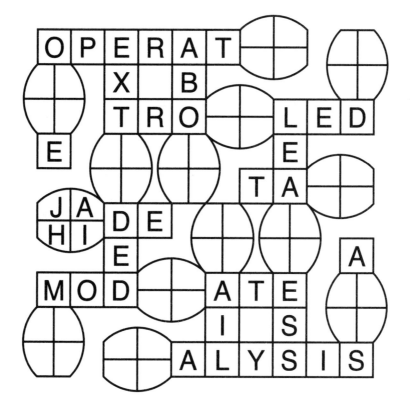

Answers on page 177.

DIY CROSSWORD

Fit the given words into the crossword grid. Be careful with your selections though—more words are provided than are needed.

ATONE

BUDDHA

CRATE

ES (chem.)

GHOST

GLOBE

GLOVE

HA

LA (musical note)

STONE

STUDIO

TI (musical note)

TIC

USA

CHAIN WORDS

Place 3 letters in the middle squares that will complete one word and start another. For example, TAR would complete GUI - TAR - GET.

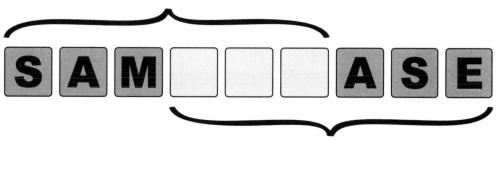

JUMBLED UP

Place each letter into the empty boxes below to create a common word. Tiles are in the correct order but they are not in the upright position.

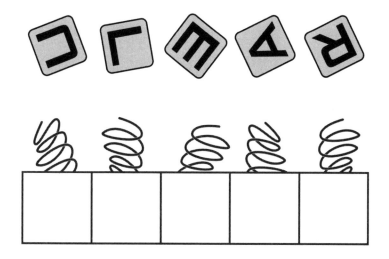

Answers on page 178.

NAME CALLING

Decipher the encoded words in the quips below using the numbers and letters on the phone pad. Remember that each number can stand for any of three or four possible letters.

1. So easy to use a child can do it. Child sold 7-3-7-2-7-2-8-3-5-9.

   _____

2. Common sense 2-4-6'-8.

   _____

3. A king's castle is 4-4-7 4-6-6-3.

   _____

4. Length, width, height, and cost are the four 3-4-6-3-6-7-4-6-6-7.

   _____

CAST-A-WORD

There are 4 dice, and there are different letters of the alphabet on the 6 faces of each of them (each letter appears only once). Random throws of the dice produced the words in this list. Can you figure out which letters appear on each of the 4 dice?

BIDE	CORK	FLAX
FORE	GNAT	HULK
INTO	MUSE	PLAN
QUAY	ROBE	STAY
TORN	VOTE	WILT

ADDAGRAM

This puzzle functions exactly like an anagram with an added step: In addition to being scrambled, each word or phrase below is missing the same letter. Discover the missing letter, then unscramble the words. When you do, you'll reveal 4 gemstones.

HAPPIER	TEA MYTH
MONOTONE	QUIT EURO

     Answers on page 178.

WORD JIGSAW

Fit the pieces into the frame to form common words reading across and down. There's no need to rotate the pieces; they'll fit as shown, with each piece used once.

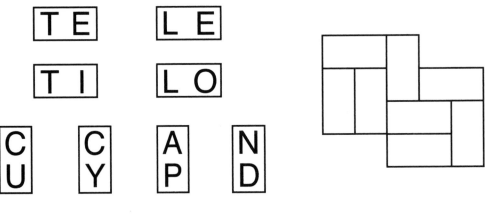

WORD LADDER

Use the clues to change just one letter on each line to go from the top word to the bottom word. Do not change the order of the letters. You must have a common English word at each step.

BRAIN

_____ down which water runs

_____ sketched by hand

_____ die in water

_____ to look down

FLOWN

ANAGRAM SENTENCES

What 2 words, formed from different arrangements of the same 4 letters, can be used to complete the sentences below?

1. She had to _____ up for weeks to have enough money to buy an antique _____.

2. The woman _____ money playing the _____ machines.

3. The _____ of cooking came through the kitchen _____.

4. She liked to _____ the skin from a _____ before eating it.

5. At the wild sorority party, the sisters dressed up a _____ in a Roman _____.

OPPOSITES

Use the letters below to fill in the boxes and reveal the 2 related words. Connected boxes share the same letter.

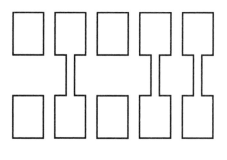

HNORSTU

Answers on page 178.

MINI-CROSS

Complete this mini crossword with the clues given below.

ACROSS

1. Big hit

6. Japanese poem

7. Someone ___ (not mine)

8. Immigrant's island

9. Very small

DOWN

1. Bed linen

2. Director Louis

3. Wedding walkway

4. Yarn on a rell

5. Brazen woman

1	2	3	4	5
6				
7				
8				
9				

LETTER TILES

Using the letter tiles, create five 5-letter words.

SAY WHAT?

Below is a group of words that, when properly arranged in the blanks, reveal a quote from Rodney Dangerfield.

other broke went fight night game

"I _____ to a _____ the

_____ _____ and a hockey

_____ _____ out."

Answers on page 178.

WORD COLUMNS

Find the hidden phrase by using the letters directly below each of the blank squares. Each letter is used only once. A black square indicates the end of a word.

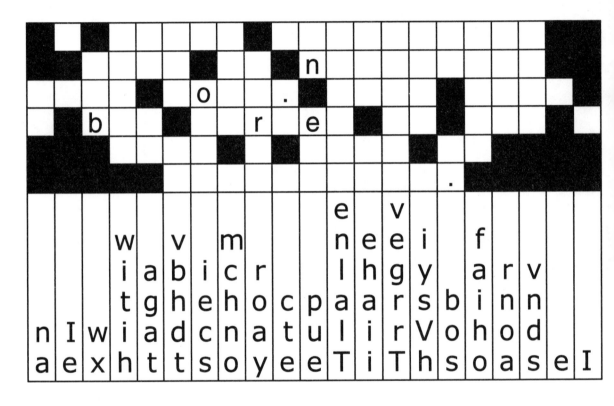

WEDGEWORDS

Fit the words into the grid reading across and down. Each word is used once.

ASAP   CLOT   CRAFT

FETE   LOSER   OVATE

ROVE   TEPEE   TREE

         Answers on page 179.

CHAIN WORDS

Place 3 letters in the middle squares that will complete one word and start another. For example, TAR would complete GUI - TAR - GET.

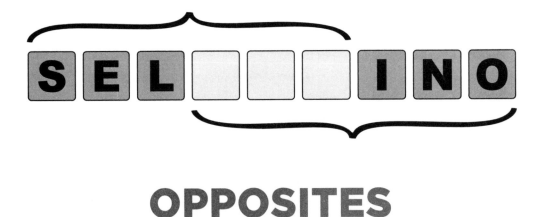

OPPOSITES

Use the letters below to fill in the boxes and reveal the 2 related words. Connected boxes share the same letter.

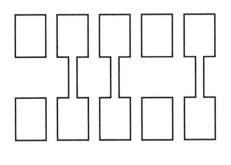

ADELRTY

ADDAGRAM

This puzzle functions exactly like an anagram with an added step: In addition to being scrambled, each word below is missing the same letter. Discover the missing letter, then unscramble the words. When you do, you'll reveal something old, a dish for serving soup, a law officer, and a word meaning "tardy."

QUAINT TUNER

COMPLAIN DEVOUR

WORD JIGSAW

Fit the pieces into the frame to form common words reading across and down. There's no need to rotate the pieces; they'll fit as shown, with each piece used once.

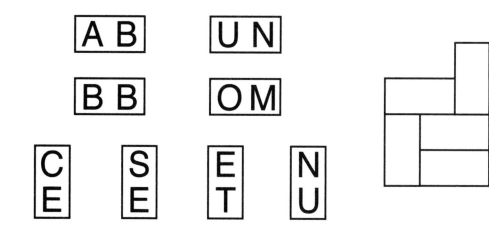

Answers on page 179.

WORD LADDER

Use the clues to change just one letter on each line to go from the top word to the bottom word. Do not change the order of the letters. You must have a common English word at each step.

BIGOT

_____ to sire

_____ the past tense of the above

_____ started before

_____ no animal produce eaten

VEGAS

ANAGRAM SENTENCES

What 2 words, formed from different arrangements of the same 4 letters, can be used to complete the sentences below?

1. My favorite _____ taught me her secret recipe for _____ casserole.

2. When you clean the _____ after preparing dinner, don't forget to clean their _____ as well.

3. The commercial for the dishwashing liquid promised it would be a _____ to clean all of your _____.

DROP-A-LETTER

Only 4 of the letters in the top line will make their way through to the bottom of this maze and land in the squares below. Once they're there, the letters will spell out the answer to this riddle:

I'm a leathery snake with a stinging bite, I'll stay coiled up unless I must fight. What am I?

Answer on page 179.

ABOUT TIME

This puzzle follows the rules of your typical word search: Every word listed is contained within the group of letters. Words can be found in a straight line horizontally, vertically, or diagonally. They may read either forward or backward. But, in this version, words wrap up, down, and around the 3 sides of the cube.

BEHIND	LUNCH	SHOW
BREAKFAST	MARKING	SMALL
CHECKOUT	MEAL	SOME
CHRISTMAS	MEAN	SPACE
CRUNCH	MOUNTAIN	SPRING
DEPARTURE	OVER	STANDARD
DINNER	PEACE	SUMMER
DOUBLE	PLAY	TRAVEL
FULL	REACTION	TURNAROUND
LEISURE	REAL	UNIVERSAL
LIFE	RESPONSE	WINTER

Answers on page 179.

DIY CROSSWORD

Fit the given words into the crossword grid. Be careful with your selections though—more words are provided than are needed.

END

EVILS

ILL

SEE

SOLID

STONE

TOO

TOW

FITTING WORDS

In this miniature crossword, the clues are listed randomly and are numbered for convenience only. It is up to you to figure out the placement of the 9 answers. To help you, we've inserted one letter in the grid, and this is the only occurrence of that letter in the completed puzzle.

CLUES

1. Laboratory bottle

2. Like the "c" in "certain"

3. Canvas shelters

4. Acts as quizmaster

5. Orchestral instruments

6. Fit for duty

7. Brazilian dance

8. Cream of the crop

9. Haunted house sound

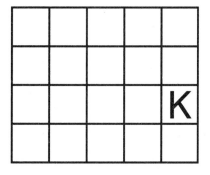

Answers on page 180.

ELEVATOR WORDS

Like an elevator, words move up and down the "floors" of this puzzle. Starting with the first answer, the second part of each answer carries down to become the first part of the following answer. With the clues given, complete the puzzle.

1. Get in _____   1. Establish communications

2. _____ _____   2. Judging criterion

3. _____ _____   3. Absolutely

4. _____ _____   4. Strong apprehension

5. _____ _____   5. 1930 Harold Lloyd movie

6. _____ _____   6. Abigail Adams and Betty Ford

7. _____ night   7. An occasion where women get discounts

Answers on page 180.   68

CHAIN WORDS

Place 3 letters in the middle squares that will complete one word and start another. For example, TAR would complete GUI - TAR - GET.

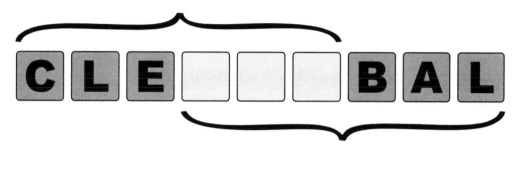

OPPOSITES

Use the letters below to fill in the boxes and reveal the 2 related words. Connected boxes share the same letter.

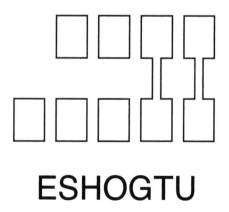

ESHOGTU

 Answers on page 180.

ANAGRAM SENTENCES

What 2 words, formed from different arrangements of the same 6 letters, can be used to complete the sentences below?

1. The _____ student could name the sculptor of every _____ in the museum.

2. Its delightful fragrance is the _____ of the _____ tree.

3. Having won two gold medals in a row, the Olympic _____ was on a winning _____.

4. She could not _____ whether she put the box of old clothes in the _____ or the attic.

LETTER TILES

Using the letter tiles, create ten 4-letter words.

CAST-A-WORD

There are 4 dice, and there are different letters of the alphabet on the 6 faces of each of them (each letter appears only once). Random throws of the dice produced the words in this list. Can you figure out which letters appear on each of the 4 dice?

BEAN	BUSY	CHEW
COLD	FIVE	JEST
PENT	PORE	QUAD
SKIN	TANG	VINE
WHIM	WIFE	

ADDAGRAM

This puzzle functions exactly like an anagram with an added step: In addition to being scrambled, each word below is missing the same letter. Discover the missing letter, then unscramble the words. When you do, you'll reveal a device used for injections, a tool used in farming, a Greek sports celebration and a word meaning exceptionally bad.

RESIGN	CHEST
DIPLOMA	BALSAM

Answers on page 180.

WORD JIGSAW

Fit the pieces into the frame to form common words reading across and down. There's no need to rotate the pieces; they'll fit as shown, with each piece used once.

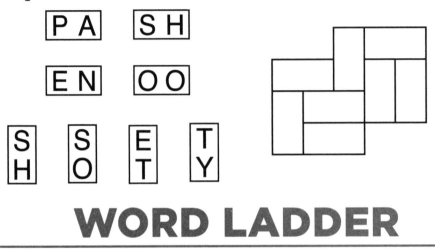

WORD LADDER

Use the clues to change just one letter on each line to go from the top word to the bottom word. Do not change the order of the letters. You must have a common English word at each step.

LOAN

_____ of bread

_____ take one from my book

_____ slender

_____ a seed

_____ tired

PEAT

CAN'T SEE THE TREES FOR THE FOREST?

Each set of words or word below contains the name of a tree. Can you find it? For example, the word "cloak" contains "oak," which is a type of tree.

1. Spine-tingling

2. Eyewitness

3. Clarence Darrow

4. Gospel music

5. Burma shave

6. Teakettle

7. Shah of Iran

8. Naval architect

Answers on page 180.

MOVIE GENRES

Use the names of the movie genres below to complete this clueless crossword grid. To help you, the genres are listed in order of the number of letters they have. The puzzle has only one solution!

5 Letters
CRIME
DRAMA

6 Letters
ACTION
COMEDY
HORROR

7 Letters
FANTASY
MYSTERY
ROMANCE

8 Letters
ANIMATED
DISASTER
THRILLER

11 Letters
DOCUMENTARY

14 Letters
SCIENCE FICTION

 Answers on page 181.

ANAGRAM SENTENCES

What 2 words, formed from different arrangements of the same
7 letters, can be used to complete the sentences below?

1. An apple was the _____ that the _____
   offered to Eve.

2. No female United States _____ has ever been
   accused of _____.

3. My mother's first trip to the art _____ was
   spoiled by her _____ to oil paint.

4. She is a happily _____ woman with a secret
   _____.

OPPOSITES

Use the letters below to fill in the boxes and reveal the 2 related words.
Connected boxes share the same letter.

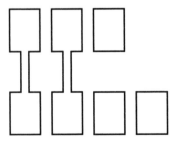

AENWX

CAST-A-WORD

There are 4 dice, and there are different letters of the alphabet on the 6 faces of each of them (each letter appears only once). Random throws of the dice produced the words in this list. Can you figure out which letters appear on each of the 4 dice?

ACME	CLIP	DREW
GOLD	GRUB	JOLT
LIFE	LION	MONK
SIGH	SIZE	STAG
VASE	YOUR	

ADDAGRAM

This puzzle functions exactly like an anagram with an added step: In addition to being scrambled, each word or phrase below is missing the same letter. Discover the missing letter, then unscramble the words. When you do, you'll reveal 4 desserts.

REFIT	DUSTER
SCRAP PIPE	BAN PINATAS

77

Answers on page 181.

DIY CROSSWORD

Fit the given words into the crossword grid. Be careful with your selections though—more words are provided than are needed.

ADO

AM

BOTTLES

COTTAGE

ICE

IT

MI

NO

PI

SPIN

TO

AGUE

ANGEL

CATCH

EN

IN

ME

MINGLED

NU

SARGE

STORAGE

TRAIN

QUOTE ME!

Rearrange 4 of the words to unscramble the quote from Albert Einstein.

"All that is valuable in individual society depends upon the development for opportunity accorded the human."

WORD TRIANGLE

Spell a 10-letter word by moving between adjacent letters. Every letter will be used at least once, but no letter will be used consecutively. Begin at any letter.

Answers on page 181.

DOUBLE JUMBLE

It's 2 jumbles in one! First, unscramble the 7 letters under each row of squares to form common English words. When you've done this, unscramble the letters running down each column in the blackened boxes to reveal 2 more words.

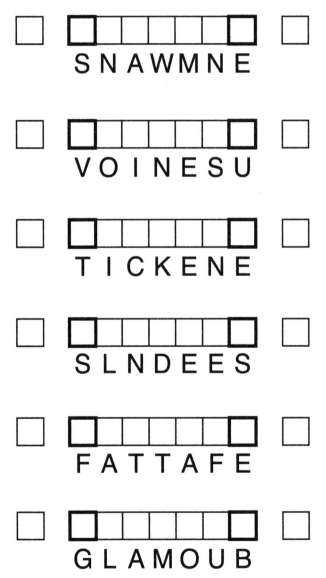

S N A W M N E

V O I N E S U

T I C K E N E

S L N D E E S

F A T T A F E

G L A M O U B

WORD LADDER

Use the clues to change just one letter on each line to go from the top word to the bottom word. Do not change the order of the letters. You must have a common English word at each step.

CRUMPET

_____ a brass instrument

_____ to be bested in competition

_____ punched

THUMBED

ANAGRAM

What are the following 3 words anagrams of?

DIAGNOSE   COUNTS   SALVAGES

A. American authors

B. American athletes

C. Countries

D. American cities

E. European cities

Answers on page 182.

WORD COLUMNS

Find the hidden humorous quote from Woody Allen by using the letters directly below each of the blank squares. Each letter is used only once. A black square indicates the end of a word.

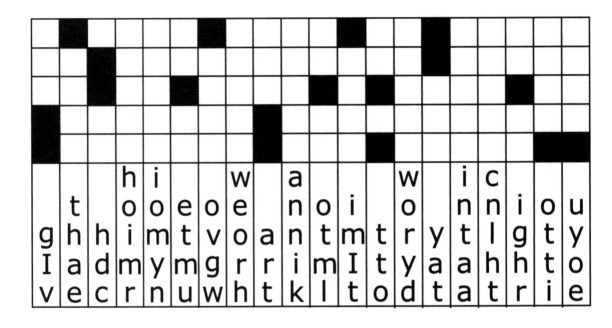

ADDAGRAM

This puzzle functions exactly like an anagram with an added step: In addition to being scrambled, each word below is missing the same letter. Discover the missing letter, then unscramble the words. When you do, you'll reveal a penguin's limb, a legal drug, something unfamiliar, and something insubstantial.

RIPPLE   FIANCEE

IGNORE   SLIMY

WORD JIGSAW

Fit the pieces into the frame to form common words reading across and down. There's no need to rotate the pieces; they'll fit as shown, with each piece used once.

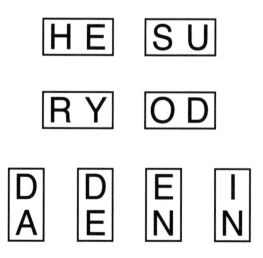

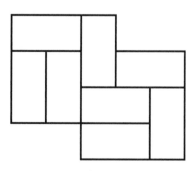

Answers on page 182.

ELEVATOR WORDS

Like an elevator, words move up and down the "floors" of this puzzle. Starting with the first answer, the second part of each answer carries down to become the first part of the following answer. With the clues given, complete the puzzle.

1. Green _____   1. Dieter's choice

2. _____ _____   2. Restaurant offering

3. _____   3. Cocktail lounge regular

4. _____ _____   4. Soar

5. _____ - _____   5. Like some gamblers

6. _____ _____   6. Baker's device

7. _____ cushion   7. Place for sewing needs

Answers on page 182.   **84**

HONEYCOMB CROSSWORD

Answer each clue with a 6-letter word. Write the words in a clockwise direction around the numbers in the grid. Words overlap each other and may start in any of the spaces around the numerals. We've placed some letters to get you started.

1. Electric signaling device

2. Obtain

3. Repeat performance

4. Eraser material

5. Coated with color

6. Talked monotonously

7. Attractive

8. Real

9. Refusal to agree

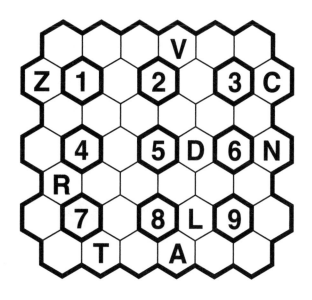

Answers on page 182.

VEGETABLE TOGS

Fill in the blank spaces as you would a crossword puzzle. The title of the puzzle might appear to be ambiguous, but it should suggest a category of words that, when linked together, will complete the puzzle.

For example, HOLE IN ONE might suggest DOUGHNUTS. Or, it might suggest GOLF, which would lead to the words CLUB, IRON, TEE, etc. But all of these words have a common theme. Notice that a few letters are already in place, and some of the words intersect —adding to the mystery, and the fun, of finding the solution.

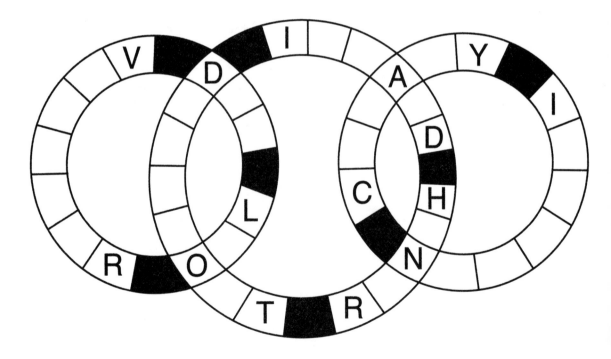

Answers on page 182.   **86**

SAY WHAT?

Below is a group of words that, when properly arranged in the blanks, reveal a quote from Ralph Waldo Emerson.

path go trail is not instead and

"Do _____ _____ where the _____

may lead, go _____ where there _____ no

path _____ leave a _____."

WORD TRIANGLE

Spell a 10-letter word by moving between adjacent letters. Every letter will be used at least once, but no letter will be used consecutively. Begin at any letter.

Answers on page 182.

ANAGRAM

Use each letter in the words below only once to spell out 3 types of fruit.

CALIBRATE   PROPER   BUYER

CHAIN WORDS

Place 3 letters in the middle squares that will complete one word and start another. For example, TAR would complete GUI - TAR - GET.

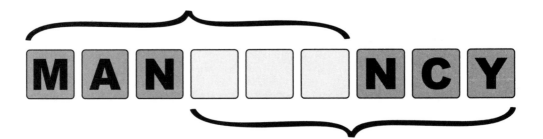

WORD LADDER

Use the clues to change just one letter on each line to go from the top word to the bottom word. Do not change the order of the letters. You must have a common English word at each step.

SMILE

_____ an old-fashioned, knightly physical blow

_____ mean-spiritedness, cruelty

_____ a tall tower which forms the roof of a building, with a pointed top

_____ where the hobbits came from

_____ an item over clothing worn over the trunk

_____ not tall

_____ things wash up on it

CHORE

Answers on page 182.

DOUBLE JUMBLE

It's 2 jumbles in one! First, unscramble the 7 letters under each row of squares to form common English words. When you've done this, unscramble the letters running down each column in the blackened boxes to reveal 2 more words.

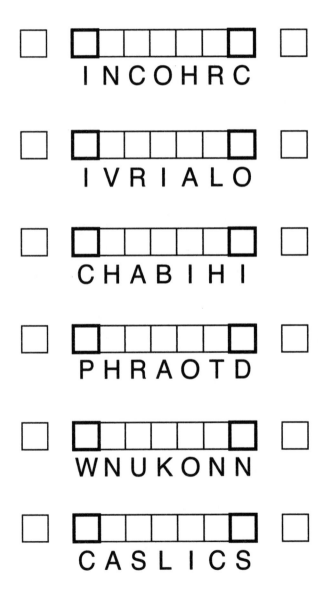

I N C O H R C

I V R I A L O

C H A B I H I

P H R A O T D

W N U K O N N

C A S L I C S

ANAGRAM CROSSWORD

Fill in the grid with anagrams (rearrangements of the same letters) of the words listed below.

ACROSS

1. SIDE CLIP

5. GO HEARTS

6. ON CANADA

7. LEAST LET

DOWN

1. IDLY PASS

2. EAST DOCK

3. CLEAN TAP

4. HEADY SEE

Answers on page 183.

CAST-A-WORD

There are 4 dice, and there are different letters of the alphabet on the 6 faces of each of them (each letter appears only once). Random throws of the dice produced the words in this list. Can you figure out which letters appear on each of the 4 dice?

BANK	CLUE	CONE
DOWN	FUSE	HOAX
JAMB	KNOW	PANT
PAVE	PUMA	SINK
TROY	WHIR	ZEBU

QUOTE ME!

Rearrange 4 of the words to unscramble the quote from Thomas Jefferson.

"A man is much more exposed to spirit than a coward of quarrels."

Answers on page 183.

SPLIT DECISIONS

Fill in each set of empty cells with letters that will create English words reading both across and down. Letters may repeat within a single set. We've completed one set to get you started.

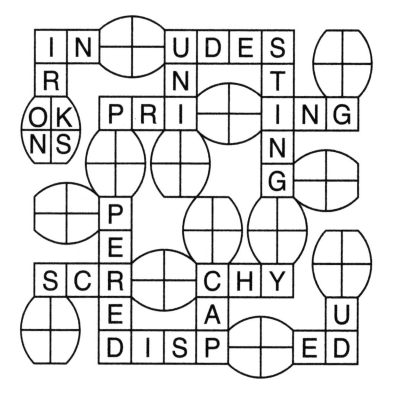

Answers on page 183.

WORD JIGSAW

Fit the pieces into the frame to form common words reading across and down. There's no need to rotate the pieces; they'll fit as shown, with each piece used once.

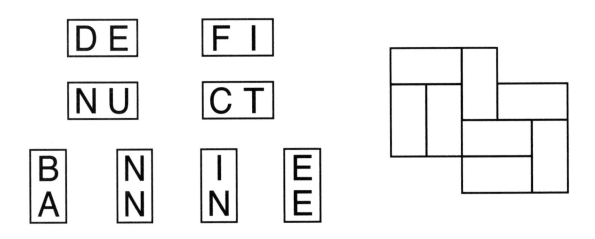

CITIES AND STATES

Without scrambling any of the original letters, spell the names of 6 U.S. cities and states by adding one letter to each word below. Letters may be inserted anywhere in the words.

FARO   INDIAN

MINE   SALE

SETTLE   TEAS

Answers on page 183.

A DARK KNIGHT

Use the clues to change just one letter on each line to go from the top word to the bottom word. Do not change the order of the letters. You must have a common English word at each step.

HEATH

_____ what an oven does to food

_____ hoists

_____ the handles of knives

_____ adult male deer

_____ a car is made up of these

_____ cuts off the outer skin

_____ how the skin breathes

_____ jabs or prods

_____ "Why did the chicken cross the road?" for one

JOKER

Answers on page 183.

TANGLED WORDS

Think of this puzzle like a word search, only in reverse. Rather than finding the words in the grid, your job is to fill them in. Words begin only from the letters given in the shaded boxes and they appear in a straight line horizontally, vertically, or diagonally. They may appear forward or backward. When complete, every word will have been used, and the grid will have no empty squares.

ADDICTS	BACKWARD	CLOAK
ADHERE	BEATNIK	DANISH
AGAIN	BLIZZARD	DECOYED
AHEAD	BOMBARD	DESCEND
AMAZED	BUZZARD	DETERMINE
ANCHOR	CARPORT	DING
ANTIC	CASH	DIPLOMA
ARTICLE	CATERER	DITCH
AVERAGE	CITIZEN	DIVER
AWARD	CIVIC	DRAINAGE

DRUID   ENIGMA   EXIST

EDDYING   ENZYMES   EXTREME

EMCEE   EPICURE

ENDORSED   EXERT

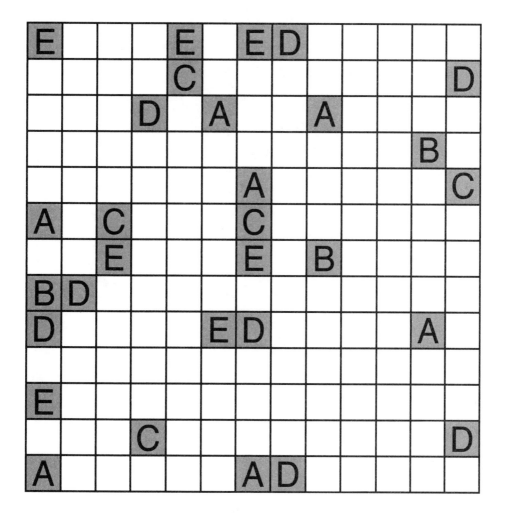

Answers on page 184.

THE STAR-SPANGLED BANNER

How many times can you read STARS in the grid by proceeding from letter to consecutive letter moving between neighboring cells?

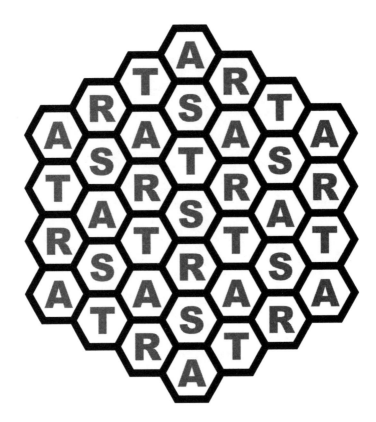

ADD-A-LETTER

Rearrange each word, adding one new letter from the bottom letters in order to form a fast food item in the empty boxes. Each letter from the bottom of the page is used only once.

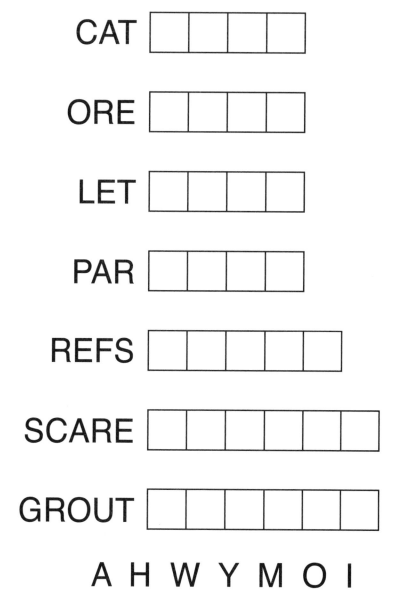

CAT

ORE

LET

PAR

REFS

SCARE

GROUT

A H W Y M O I

Answers on page 184.

CAST-A-WORD

There are 4 dice, and there are different letters of the alphabet on the 6 faces of each of them (each letter appears only once). Random throws of the dice produced the words in this list. Can you figure out which letters appear on each of the 4 dice?

ACHE	DOZY	FINE
JOKE	LINE	NECK
NEWT	ONYX	PAIL
QUIZ	SWAT	TRAM
URGE		

ADDAGRAM

This puzzle functions exactly like an anagram with an added step: In addition to being scrambled, each word below is missing the same letter. Discover the missing letter, then unscramble the words. When you do, you'll reveal a small bomb, a seasonal immune system sensitivity, a dwarf, and a something denoted by vertical lines on a map.

ENDEAR   REALLY

TIMED   OUTLINED

Answers on page 184.   **100**

WORD JIGSAW

Fit the pieces into the frame to form common words reading across and down. There's no need to rotate the pieces; they'll fit as shown, with each piece used once.

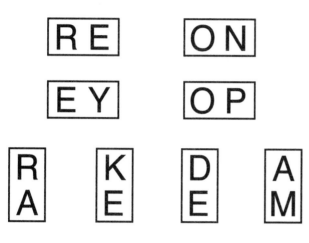

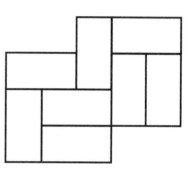

OPPOSITES

Use the letters below to fill in the boxes and reveal the 2 related words. Connected boxes share the same letter.

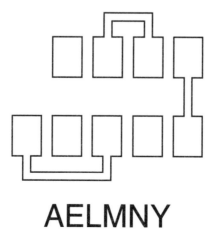

AELMNY

Answers on page 184.

THE PRINCESS OF MONACO

Use the clues to change just one letter on each line to go from the top word to the bottom word. Do not change the order of the letters. You must have a common English word at each step.

GRACE

_____ A, B or C

_____ June honorees

_____ small fastener (plural)

_____ necklace components

_____ call on a coin toss

_____ recovers

_____ prepares for posting

_____ hawks

_____ they ring

_____ stomach

KELLY

ELEVATOR WORDS

Like an elevator, words move up and down the "floors" of this puzzle. Starting with the first answer, the second part of each answer carries down to become the first part of the following answer. With the clues given, complete the puzzle.

1. Mother _____   1. Imaginary nursery rhymes author

2. _____ _____   2. Zero

3. _____ _____   3. Sweetened milk drink

4. _____ _____   4. Pasta topper

5. _____   5. Small pot

6. _____   6. Breakfast choice

7. _____ mix   7. Baker's convenience

Answers on page 184.

STEPWORDS

This is a crossword puzzle with a twist. Use the clues to solve the puzzle. When complete, unscramble the circled letters to spell out a mystery word.

ACROSS

1. Catch a wave
2. Lifeguard's warning
3. Breast _____
4. Lie in the water
5. Head first entry
6. Mixed with Coke
7. _____ the beach

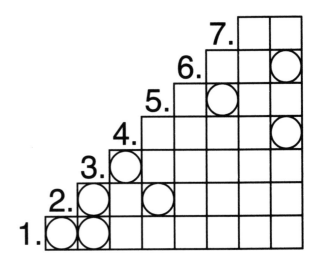

Mystery word: _____

ALPHABET SOUP

In this bowl of soup, there is at least one alphabet set (A to Z) swirling around. There are some extra letters given as well. Find the extra letters and unscramble them to reveal a girl's name.

Answer on page 184.

WORD JIGSAW

Fit the pieces into the frame to form common words reading across and down. There's no need to rotate the pieces; they'll fit as shown, with each piece used once.

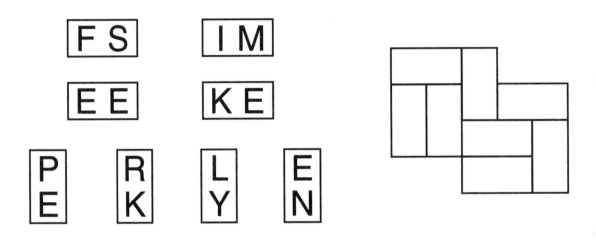

ADDAGRAM

This puzzle functions exactly like an anagram with an added step: In addition to being scrambled, each word below is missing the same letter. Discover the missing letter, then unscramble the words. When you do, you'll reveal a color, a form of government, a record of historical events, and a word relating to atomic energy.

MINORS   HARMONY

CHLORINE   UNREAL

HONEYCOMB CROSSWORD

Answer each clue with a 6-letter word. Write the words in a clockwise direction around the numerals in the grid. Words overlap each other and may start in any of the spaces around the numerals. We've placed some letters to get you started.

1. Former Spanish dictator

2. Set afloat

3. Native of Tripoli

4. Hit out of bounds

5. Leftover

6. Shamelessly bold

7. Merchant

8. Small, intricate part

9. Least dangerous

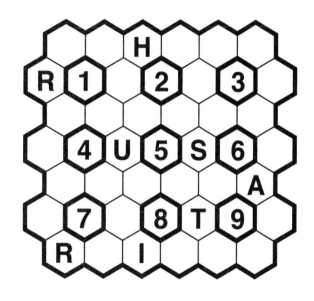

Answers on page 185.

MIND STRETCHER

Enter letters into the empty circles so that the given word can be spelled out in order from letter to consecutive letter through connected circles.

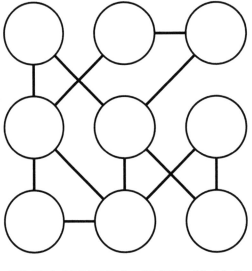

FOURTH OF JULY

WORD TRIO

Fill in each white square with a different letter so a trio of related words is formed.

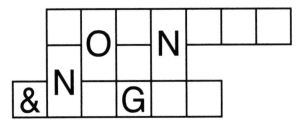

WORD JIGSAW

Fit the pieces into the frame to form common words reading across and down. There's no need to rotate the pieces; they'll fit as shown, with each piece used once.

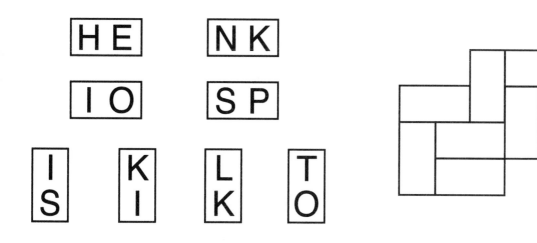

CHAIN WORDS

Place 3 letters in the middle squares that will complete one word and start another. For example, TAR would complete GUI - TAR - GET.

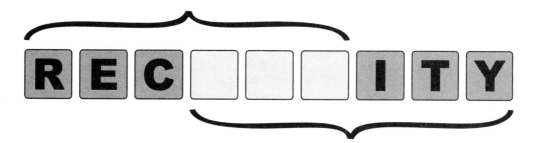

Answers on page 185.

"HI-YO, SILVER, AWAY!"

Use the clues to change just one letter on each line to go from the top word to the bottom word. Do not change the order of the letters. You must have a common English word at each step.

RANGER

_____ look-alike

_____ stick around

_____ more extended

_____ roomer

_____ The Artful _____

_____ walk unsteadily

_____ silo holdings

_____ file holder

_____ electrician's alloy

_____ you, when you complete this

SILVER

CODEWORD

The letters of the alphabet are hidden in code: Each is represented by a random number from 1 through 26. With the letters already given, complete the crossword puzzle with English words and break the code.

18	21	4	11	5	25	26	24	■	5	16	19	15
12	■	24	■	12	■	10	■	■	■	11	■	26
5	19	24	26	3	■	21	9	26	16	21	24	16
14	■	19	■	3	■	4	■	■	4	■	■	14
■	■	6	■	21	■	2	26	8	26	16	21	10
8	26	5	12	5	21	5	■	26	■	6	■	11
4	■	■	■	5	■	■	■	24	■	■	■	4
11	■	4	■	19	■	23	11	21	9	26	21	15
11	21	8	19	11	5	21	■	20	■	24	■	■
26	■	19	■	■	■	24	■	26	■	13	■	7
4	17	12	4	16	26	3	■	21	22	12	10	21
1	■	24	■	■	■	26	■	2	■	11	■	12
21	4	16	5	■	1	2	4	10	24	21	5	5

A B C D E F G H I J K L M N O P Q R S T U V W X Y Z

1	2	3	4	5	6	7	8	9	10	11	12	13
				S			M				U	J

14	15	16	17	18	19	20	21	22	23	24	25	26
H												

Answers on page 185.

STEPWORDS

This is a crossword puzzle with a twist. Use the clues to solve the puzzle. When complete, unscramble the circled letters to spell out a mystery word.

ACROSS

1. Bright flash
2. Used to fire missiles
3. Fiery sky aura
4. Lights explosive
5. Explosive cover
6. Sound of fuse burning

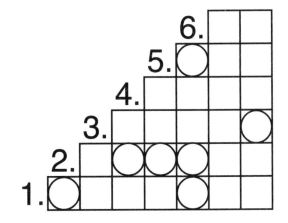

Mystery word: _____

BREEZY NEWS

Cryptograms are messages in substitution code. Break the code to read the humorous message. For example, THE SMART CAT might become FVO QWGDF JGF if **F** is substituted for **T**, **V** for **H**, **O** for **E**, and so on.

JVTF UFT EUUB GVRCG, NFUCVTB

UDTFG —JVSZV OTNFG MUR ASYT SF

N EBNWCM VURGT.

MIND STRETCHER

Enter letters into the empty circles so that the given word can be spelled out in order from letter to consecutive letter through connected circles. Letters can be used more than once.

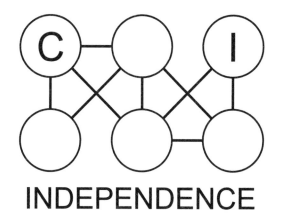

INDEPENDENCE

Answers on page 186.

DOUBLED UP

This puzzle works exactly like a crossword, except instead of placing one letter in each box, you place two. Words are written across in each box. As a bonus, unscramble the letters found in the shaded boxes to answer the definition below.

ACROSS

1. Smoked, seasoned beef
5. Wine carafe
6. Nice
8. On a slant
10. Lobby, hall
11. Manner, stance

DOWN

2. Loud, harsh
3. Effort
4. Absolute
7. Wet through
8. Envoy, attache
9. Height

One out of several: _____

Answers on page 186.

WORD LADDER

Change just one letter on each line to go from the top word to the bottom word. Do not change the order of the letters. You must have a common English word at each step.

BLOCK

_____

_____

_____

_____

START

DECORATIVE WORD

Plug in the appropriate 7 consonants to find the word.

O A E A I O

WEDGEWORDS

Fit the words into the grid reading across and down. Each word is used once.

DEER

IDEA

RITE

EIDER

PEST

STEER

ERRS

PRIDE

TEARS

Answers on page 186.

DIS CON NEC TED

Use the clues to fill in the blanks with words (or abbreviations) that tie into the clue. We've done the first one for you.

Then, rearrange some of those words to discover a mystery word that relates to this definition: cult of consumers. The words aren't in any particular order, but they all contain letters that are found in the mystery word.

1. Exists: is

2. Sea (in French): ____ ____ ____

3. Company (abbr.): ____ ____

4. Small (abbr.) ____ ____

5. Thank you (in French): ____ ____ ____ ____ ____

6. Boxer who was Clay: ____ ____ ____

7. Internet business, with dot: ____ ____ ____

Mystery word: _____

CAST-A-WORD

There are 4 dice, and there are different letters of the alphabet on the 6 faces of each of them (each letter appears only once). Random throws of the dice produced the words in this list. Can you figure out which letters appear on each of the 4 dice?

BEAU	BUSH	CLEF
DRIP	FADE	FARM
GUST	JIVE	MAZE
ONLY	TACK	THUS
VENT	WINE	YARD

ADDAGRAM

This puzzle functions exactly like an anagram with an added step: In addition to being scrambled, each word below is missing the same letter. Discover the missing letter, then unscramble the words. When you do, you'll reveal a type of publication, a cooking formula, a word meaning "to imitate," and a synonym for "pervious."

AMAZING	PRICE
AMULET	PREAMBLE

WORD JIGSAW

Fit the pieces into the frame to form common words reading across and down. There's no need to rotate the pieces; they'll fit as shown, with each piece used exactly once.

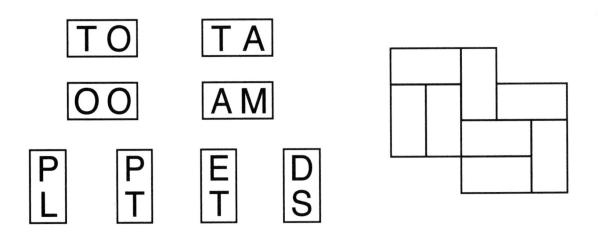

GAME CHANGE

Is it possible to exchange just 2 letters in this word to get another word?

GAME

WORD LADDER

Use the clues to change just one letter on each line to go from the top word to the bottom word. Do not change the order of the letters. You must have a common English word at each step.

BASE

_____ type of guitar

_____ get hits with these

_____ every team wears them

HITS

LETTER TILES

Using the letter tiles, create five 5-letter words.

Answers on page 187.

AFRICA

This puzzle follows the rules of your typical word search: Every country listed is contained within the group of letters. Words can be found in a straight line horizontally, vertically, or diagonally. They may read either forward or backward. But, in this version, words wrap up, down, and around the 3 sides of the cube.

ALGERIA	ETHIOPIA	NAMIBIA
ANGOLA	GABON	SENEGAL
BENIN	GAMBIA	SIERRA LEONE
BOTSWANA	GHANA	SOUTH AFRICA
BURKINA FASO	KENYA	SWAZILAND
CHAD	LIBERIA	TOGO
CÔTE D'IVOIRE	LIBYA	TUNISIA
DJIBOUTI	MOROCCO	ZAMBIA
EGYPT	MOZAMBIQUE	ZIMBABWE

Answers on page 187.

ELEVATOR WORDS

Like an elevator, words move up and down the "floors" of this puzzle. Starting with the first answer, the second part of each answer carries down to become the first part of the following answer. With the clues given, complete the puzzle.

1. Watered-_____   1. Moire

2. _____ _____   2. Kapok

3. _____ _____   3. Spun sugar treat

4. _____ _____   4. It's coated with taffy
                                   and served on a stick

5. _____ _____   5. Toast topper

6. _____ _____   6. Serving piece

7. _____ rack   7. Draining aid

Answers on page 187.

ACTORS SCRAMBLEGRAM

Four 7-letter words, all of which revolve around the same theme, have been jumbled. Unscramble each word, and write the answer in the accompanying space. Next, transfer the letters in the shaded boxes into the shaded keyword spaces, and unscramble the 6-letter word that goes with the theme. The theme for this puzzle is leading men, past and present.

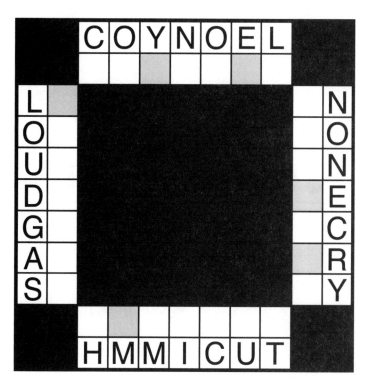

KEYWORD

Answers on page 187.

DEAR DIARY

Cryptograms are messages in substitution code. Break the code to read the message. For example, THE SMART CAT might become FVO QWGDF JGF if **F** is substituted for **T, V** for **H, O** for **E,** and so on.

"Q TZUZY PYCUZN BQPVRWP JL

AQCYL. RTZ GVRWNA CNBCLG VCUZ

GRJZPVQTH GZTGCPQRTCN PR YZCA."

— RGECY BQNAZ

JUMBLED UP

Place each letter into the empty boxes below to create a common word. Tiles are in the correct order but they are not in the upright position.

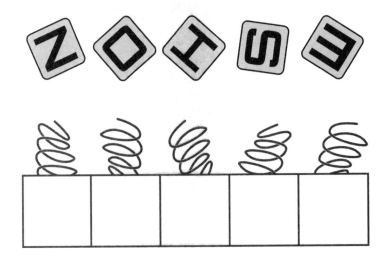

GRID FILL

To complete this puzzle, place the given list of letters and words into the shapes in this grid. Words and letters will run across, down, and wrap around each shape. When the grid is filled, each row will contain one of the following words: bench, fan, bat, stadium, teams, umpires, catcher.

1. A, T, U

2. AT, BE, RS, ST

3. ERE, SUM

4. BEAM, CAMP, INCH

5. DITCH

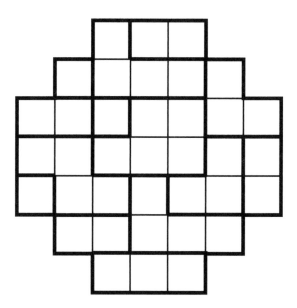

Answers on page 187.

STILL A HERO

Change just one letter on each line to go from the top word to the bottom word. Do not change the order of the letters. You must have a common English word or a name at each step.

FORD

_____

_____

_____

SOLO

REWORD REWIND

Unscramble the tiles to form words that will complete the sentence.

The _____ were neat, but the lion was the _____ of the zoo.

A T R S

NOT QUITE A CROSSWORD SNACK

This is a crossword puzzle with a twist. Use the clues to solve the puzzle. When complete, the circled letters will spell out a mystery word.

ACROSS

1. Good use for food coloring

2. Easter procession

3. Eggs and candy holder at Easter

4. Child looking for Easter eggs, e.g.

5. Easter topper

6. Easter lily or daffodil

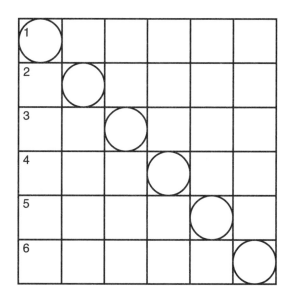

Answers on page 187.

HOCKEY TEAMS

Put 1 or 2 letters in each white square so that each word in the list provided is spelled out either horizontally or vertically. Additionally, the 3 outlined boxes contain the same single letter. We've filled in a square to get you started.

AVALANCHE

BLACKHAWKS

BLUES

CANUCKS

DUCKS

KINGS

OILERS

PREDATORS

STARS

WILD

CAST-A-WORD

There are 4 dice, and there are different letters of the alphabet on the 6 faces of each of them (each letter appears only once). Random throws of the dice produced the words in this list. Can you figure out which letters appear on each of the 4 dice?

BOWL	CAMP	CAVE	HOCK
JOIN	PINK	PURE	QUAY
RISE	SELF	STUB	TIDE
VINY	ZONE		

WORD JIGSAW

Fit the pieces into the frame to form common words reading across and down. There's no need to rotate the pieces; they'll fit as shown, with each piece used exactly once. Hint: The 4-letter word in the middle column is a word related to hockey.

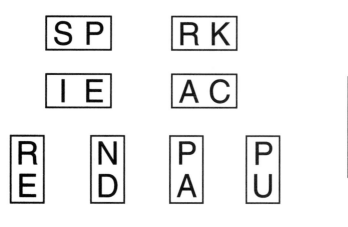

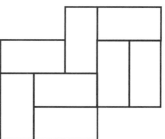

Answers on page 188.

MISSING CONNECTIONS

It's a crossword without the clues! Use the letters below to fill in the empty spaces in the crossword grid. When you are finished, you'll have words that read both across and down, crossword-style.

A A A B B C C E E E E E G I I I L M N O R R T T

WORD COLUMNS

Find the hidden quote from John F. Kennedy using the letters directly below each of the blank squares. Each letter is used only once. A black square indicates the end of a word.

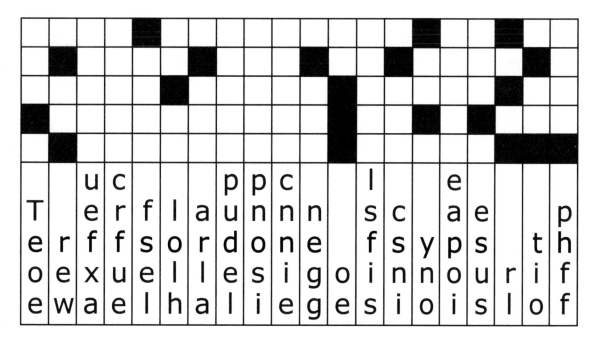

Answer on page 188.

FITTING WORDS

In this miniature crossword, the clues are listed randomly and are numbered for convenience only. It is up to you to figure out the placement of the 9 answers. To help you, we've inserted two letters in the grid, and this is the only occurrence of those letters in the completed puzzle.

1. Homes for birds

2. Small brown songbird

3. Use the pink end of a pencil

4. "Woe is me!"

5. Huge ocean mammal

6. They have lenses, irises, and corneas

7. In this spot

8. Final

9. Type of race in which you pass a baton

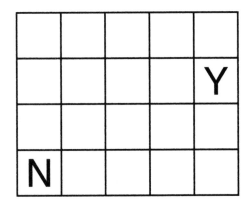

Answers on page 188.

ADDAGRAM

This puzzle functions exactly like an anagram with an added step: In addition to being scrambled, each word below is missing the same letter. Discover the missing letter, then unscramble the words. When you do, you'll reveal a game plan, a gap between nerve cells, a word for motherhood, and an adjective meaning "deserving."

TARGETS   ASPENS

MARTINET   THROW

WORD JIGSAW

Fit the pieces into the frame to form common words reading across and down. There's no need to rotate the pieces; they'll fit as shown, with each piece used once.

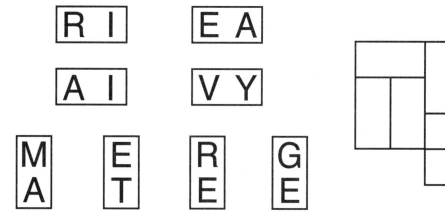

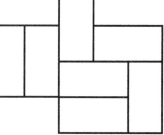

Answers on page 188.

QUIRKS OF THE CHAMPS

Cryptograms are messages in substitution code. Break the code to read the sports factoid. For example, THE SMART CAT might become FVO QWGDF JGF if **F** is substituted for **T, V** for **H, O** for **E,** and so on.

S Z I E I J I K Z I Q Y L T I X A E L P L U D Z ,

U I E E A V D Z L P Q C A P P T D W E E W K V

M I Q U L E W U I H K W P Z A V

R K L E X P W U Z I K U O D M I X A E U W Z A V

V W D M H W K Y O D M .

WORD LADDER

Change just one letter on each line to go from the top word to the bottom word. Do not change the order of the letters. You must have a common English word at each step.

GOLD

_____

_____ what you toss in the washer

_____

LEAF

 Answers on page 188.

WEDGEWORDS

Fit the words into the grid reading across and down. Each word is used once.

AMIDE

AMIR

BITE

CART

CABIN

NEST

TREAT

RITES

IDEA

DOUBLED UP

This puzzle works exactly like a crossword, except instead of placing one letter in each box, you place two. Words are written across in each box. As a bonus, unscramble the letters found in the shaded boxes to answer the definition below.

ACROSS

1. Release
5. Twilight
6. A type of armchair
8. Investigates
10. Cleric
11. Well-informed

DOWN

2. Congregation member
3. News posting
4. Quietude
7. Idle
8. Prolonged
9. Accompanied

Beside the point:_____

139

A TO Z

Enter every letter of the alphabet into the grid below. Letters are consecutively diagonally, horizontally, or vertically, from A to Z. Use the clue to fill in the circles and help complete the grid.

Clue: Two American colors

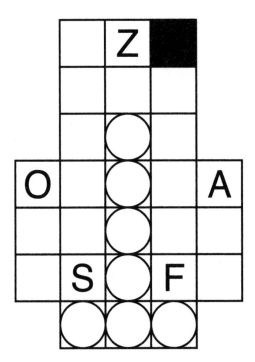

Answer on page 189.

PROFESSIONAL SCRAMBLEGRAM

Four 11-letter words, all of which revolve around the same theme, have been jumbled. Unscramble each word, and write the answer in the accompanying space. Next, transfer the letters in the shaded boxes into the shaded keyword space, and unscramble the 9-letter word that goes with the theme. The theme for this puzzle is professions.

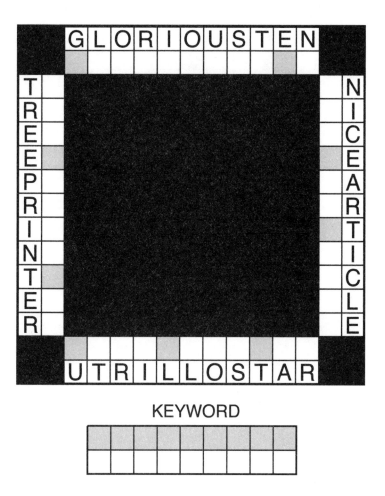

GLORIOUSTEN

TREEPRINTER

NICEARTICLE

UTRILLOSTAR

KEYWORD

WORD COLUMNS

Find the hidden phrase by using the letters directly below each of the blank squares. Each letter is used only once. A black square or the end of the line indicates the end of a word.

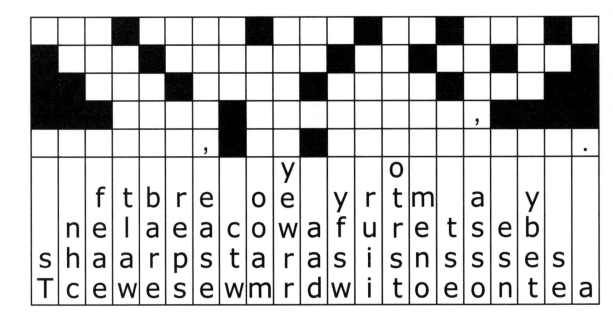

Answer on page 189.

MISSING CONNECTIONS

It's a crossword without the clues! Use the letters below to fill in the empty spaces in the crossword grid. When you are finished, you'll have words that read both across and down, crossword-style.

A A A B B D D E F G I L N P P P P R R R S S T Y

FITTING WORDS

In this miniature crossword, the clues are listed randomly and are numbered for convenience only. It is up to you to figure out the placement of the 9 answers. To help you, we've inserted one letter in the grid, and this is the only occurrence of that letter in the completed puzzle.

1. Rust, e.g.

2. Apple cofounder

3. Take the helm

4. Upper hand

5. Eat and eat and eat

6. Wolfish look

7. Sangria ingredient

8. Precious stone

9. Stage direction

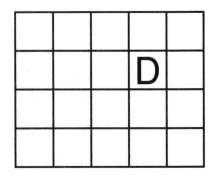

Answers on page 189

ALPHABET SOUP

In this bowl of soup, there is at least one alphabet set (A to Z) swirling around. There are some extra letters given as well. Find the extra letters and unscramble them to reveal a boy's name.

TOP SPIN

There are 5 five-sided spinning tops and there are different letters of the alphabet on each of them (each letter appears only once). All 5 tops are spun at the same time. When the tops come to rest, the following words can be created. Can you figure out which letters appear on each of the 5 tops?

AILED	BROWN	CRAWL
CRUST	DUPES	FLICK
GAZED	LAGER	MAJOR
MINOR	PIQUE	SHORT
STOKE	VINER	VIXEN

ADDAGRAM

This puzzle functions exactly like an anagram with an added step: In addition to being scrambled, each word below is missing the same letter. Discover the missing letter, then unscramble the words. When you do, you'll reveal a catastrophe, a turning point, a mythical creature, and a musical instrument.

GYRATE	WEATHERS
GROAN	NOMINAL

Answers on page 190.

WORD JIGSAW

Fit the pieces into the frame to form words reading across and down. There's no need to rotate the pieces; they'll fit as shown, with each piece used once. Note: one of the words in the grid is a place mentioned in the Bible.

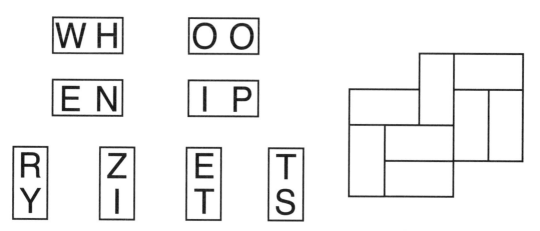

YOU HEARD IT HERE FIRST!

Cryptograms are messages in substitution code. Break the code to read the message. For example, THE SMART CAT might become FVO QWGDF JGF if **F** is substituted for **T,** V for **H, O** for **E,** and so on.

AW AY AX MNY R QNV AY JAGG QS R

CADG, XRVX YES WNDYLMS-YSGGSD.

—KRBRCRXZRD ODNHSDQ

ANALOGIES

Study the relationships of the word pairs to discover what's missing.

1. Downpour is to drizzle as wind is to _____.

   A. rain

   B. weather

   C. breeze

2. Dream is to sleep as _____ is to hayfever.

   A. illness

   B. sneeze

   C. ragweed

3. Push is to shove as pull is to _____.

   A. hoist

   B. slide

   C. yank

4. Online is to Internet as surfing is to _____.

   A. web

   B. beach

   C. wind

Answers on page 190

A TO Z

Enter every letter of the alphabet into the grid below. Letters are connected horizontally, vertically, or diagonally from A to Z. Use the clue to fill in the circles and help complete the grid.

Clue: Numbers

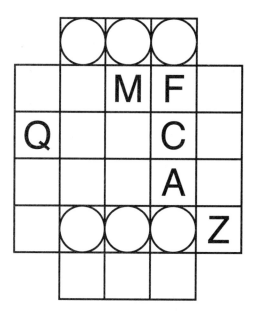

CODEWORD

The letters of the alphabet are hidden in code: Each is represented by a random number from 1 through 26. With the letters already given, complete the crossword puzzle with English words and break the code.

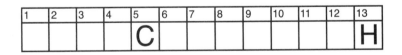

A B C D E F G H I J K L M N O P Q R S T U V W X Y Z

1	2	3	4	5	6	7	8	9	10	11	12	13
				C								H

14	15	16	17	18	19	20	21	22	23	24	25	26
E								V				

Answers on page 190

BUNNY ZIGZAG

Trace a path passing through each square exactly once, spelling the word bunny along the way. The path travels diagonally, horizontally, and vertically, and it never crosses itself.

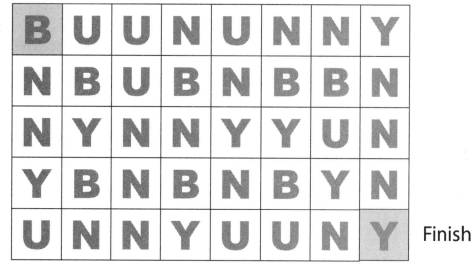

Start

B	U	U	N	U	N	N	Y
N	B	U	B	N	B	B	N
N	Y	N	N	Y	Y	U	N
Y	B	N	B	N	B	Y	N
U	N	N	Y	U	U	N	Y

Finish

REWORD REWIND

Unscramble the tiles to form new words that will complete the sentence.

The athlete wanted to _____ for shoes to make her _____ and leaps higher.

O S P H

VISUALIZE THIS!

I have planted a variety of vegetables in rows in my garden, and am proceeding from the front of my garden to the back, picking them. I planted the leeks almost at the back of the garden, in front of the peas, separated from them by the tomatoes. The second row contains the cabbages, and the row one behind these contains spinach. Rhubarb is not planted in the last row, but is amongst the first 3 rows. The mange tout is beyond the spinach, but before the leeks. Behind the spinach are 2 rows containing the carrots, and behind these the beetroot. In what order do I find the vegetables as I progress from the front to the back? The first row contains beans; the last row contains brussels sprouts.

Answer on page 190.

ADDAGRAM

This puzzle functions exactly like an anagram with an added step: In addition to being scrambled, each word below is missing the same letter. Discover the missing letter, then unscramble the words. When you do, you'll reveal pincers, a metal, a fast-running animal, and a native of a country.

SWEETER   BORNE

ALLEGE   INCITE

WORD JIGSAW

Fit the pieces into the frame to form words reading across and down. There's no need to rotate the pieces; they'll fit as shown, with each piece used once. Note: One of the words in the grid is a place mentioned in the Bible.

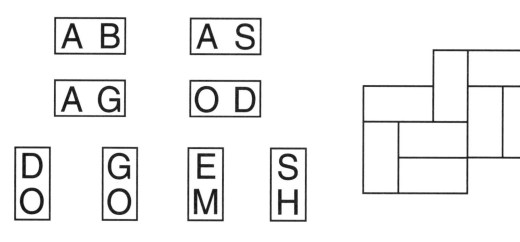

CROSSED WORDS

Unscramble the words in each line to solve the puzzle. The words cross on a letter that they share.

Clue: Fractionally under and shared

```
            O
            C
R E T I M N O A N O D
            N
            M
            O
```

GOOD EATS UP NORTH

Cryptograms are messages in substitution code. Break the code to read the food fact. For example, THE SMART CAT might become FVO QWGDF JGF if **F** is substituted for **T**, **V** for **H**, **O** for **E**, and so on

ZHNELTU, O ZHZNKOG IHYRHGE

RHHP LT IOTOPO, LB RGUTIV RGLUB

EHZZUP MLEV RGUBV IVUUBU

INGPB, EVUT IHQUGUP MLEV CGHMT

WGOQX.

  Answers on page 191.

FITTING WORDS

In this miniature crossword, the clues are listed randomly and are numbered for convenience only. It is up to you to figure out the placement of the 9 answers. To help you, we've inserted one letter in the grid, and this is the only occurrence of that letter in the completed puzzle.

1. Pittsburgh product

2. Fuming

3. Decisive victory

4. _____ of Sandwich

5. You, once

6. Chocolate-coffee flavor

7. Little devils

8. 43,560 square feet

9. More pristine

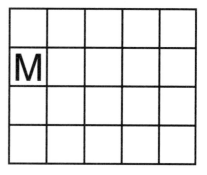

SPLIT DECISIONS

Fill in each set of empty cells with letters that will create English words reading both across and down. Letters may repeat within a single set. We've completed one set to get you started.

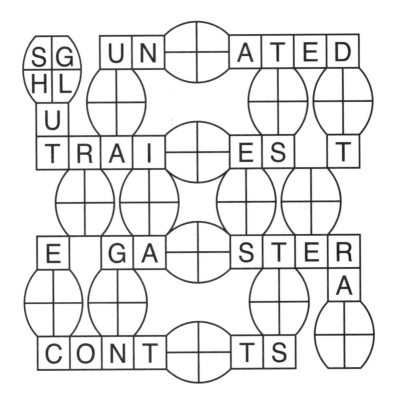

Answers on page 191

ELEVATOR WORDS

Like an elevator, words move up and down the "floors" of this puzzle. Starting with the first answer, the second part of each answer carries down to become the first part of the following answer. With the clues given, complete the puzzle.

1. Diamond_____   1. Rattler

2. _____   2. Isolated place

3. _____ _____   3. Upper limit of a portion
                                  of saturated ground

4. _____ _____   4. Something to serve
                                  with dinner

5. _____ _____   5. Refreshing party
                                  beverage

6. _____ _____   6. Forecast in the fall

7. _____ the storm   7. Successfully deal with
                                  a difficult situation

MISSING CONNECTIONS

It's a crossword without the clues! Use the letters below to fill in the empty spaces in the crossword grid. When you are finished, you'll have words that read both across and down, crossword-style.

A B B C C E E E G H I N P R R R R S T T

Answers on page 191.

RHYME TIME

Each clue leads to a 2-word answer that rhymes, such as BIG PIG or STABLE TABLE. The numbers in parentheses after the clue give the number of letters in each word. For example, "cookware taken from the oven (3, 3)" would be "hot pot."

1. Unusual alteration (7, 6): _____ _____

2. Play area for Jaws and friends (5, 4): _____ _____

3. Avenue or boulevard a cut above the rest (5, 6): _____ _____

4. Made-up malady (4, 4): _____ _____

5. Dark-red party favor full of helium (6, 7): _____ _____

6. Acuity with burgers and brats (5, 5): _____ _____

7. Celebrated latticework pastries (5, 4): _____ _____

8. Select opinions (6, 5): _____ _____

Answers on page 191.

DOUBLED UP

This puzzle works exactly like a crossword, except instead of placing one letter in each box, you place two. Words are written across in each box. As a bonus, unscramble the letters found in the shaded boxes to answer the definition below.

ACROSS

1. Momentous, notable
5. French ruler
6. Get familiar with
8. A soft wool
10. Giving
11. Lengthen

DOWN

2. Unmoving
3. Middle of the day
4. Elegant, poised
7. A jet is one
8. Merry-go-round
9. Refurbish

Draws for a smile: _____

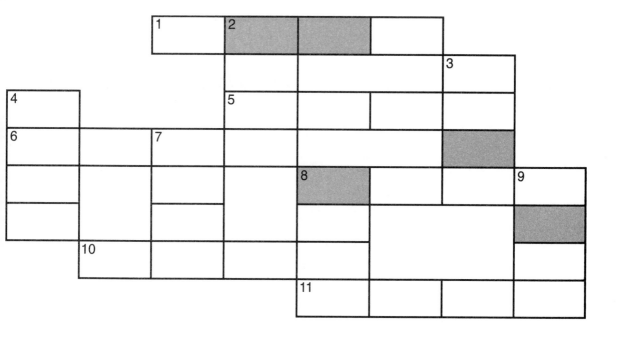

GREEDY SCRAMBLEGRAM

Four 11-letter words, all of which revolve around the same theme, have been jumbled. Unscramble each word, and write the answer in the accompanying space. Next, transfer the letters in the shaded boxes into the shaded keyword space, and unscramble the 9-letter word that goes with the theme. The theme for this puzzle is money.

NOITEMTOPIC

POORARTICON

HIDMENACERS

ROCKTOKERBS

KEYWORD

CAST-A-WORD

There are 4 dice, and there are different letters of the alphabet on the 6 faces of each of them (each letter appears only once). Random throws of the dice produced the words in this list. Can you figure out which letters appear on each of the 4 dice?

ATOM	BLIP	BUNG
CREW	JEST	JINK
LORD	PAVE	SAIL
SURF	SWIM	WHEY
X-RAY		

WORD JIGSAW

Fit the pieces into the frame to form words reading across and down. There's no need to rotate the pieces; they'll fit as shown, with each piece used once. Note: One of the words in the grid is a place mentioned in the Bible.

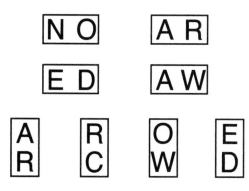

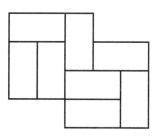

ODD ONE OUT

Can you determine which of the words below is the odd one out?

Hint: Think about structures.

ANNA   BOB   DAVID   HANNAH

ABC

Fill in each individual block with the letters A, B, and C. No letter should be adjacent to itself—horizontally or vertically—between blocks.

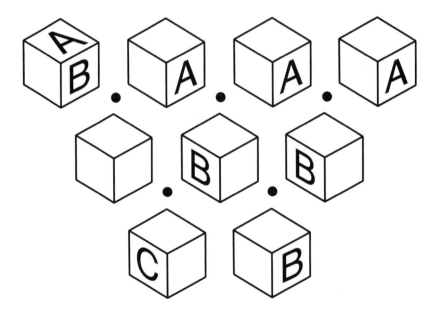

Answers on page 192.

CAST-A-WORD

There are 4 dice, and there are different letters of the alphabet on the 6 faces of each of them (each letter appears only once). Random throws of the dice produced the words in this list. Can you figure out which letters appear on each of the 4 dice?

BALK	BLOG	CLEF	CUTE
DIAL	FERN	HIVE	JUST
PEAT	QUOD	ROTE	SWAT
TEAL	TUCK	WAXY	WHEY

ADDAGRAM

This puzzle functions exactly like an anagram with an added step: In addition to being scrambled, each word below is missing the same letter. Discover the missing letter, then unscramble the words. When you do, you'll reveal a ceremony, something central, profitable, and charitable.

TRAIL	UNCLES
VERTICAL	MISTRAL

FITTING WORDS

In this miniature crossword, the clues are listed randomly and are numbered for convenience only. It is up to you to figure out the placement of the 9 answers. To help you, we've inserted one letter in the grid, and this is the only occurrence of that letter in the completed puzzle.

1. Scoundrel

2. Hawaiian port

3. "If all _____ fails..."

4. Boot-shaped country

5. Lacking slack

6. Colored, like Easter eggs

7. Couldn't stand

8. Chose

9. On

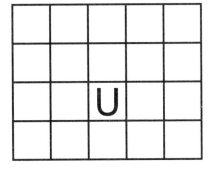

Answers on page 192.

ANALOGIES

Study the relationships of the word pairs to discover what's missing.

1. Arizona is to Phoenix as Kansas is to _____.

   A. Maine

   B. prairie

   C. Topeka

2. Stone is to catapult as ball is to _____.

   A. catcher

   B. pitcher

   C. umpire

3. Persian is to _____ as bloodhound is to dog.

   A. snake

   B. hippo

   C. cat

4. Roller coaster is to theme park as _____ is to marina.

   A. sailboat

   B. car

   C. motorcycle

Answers on page 192. **167**

OH, NO-O-O-O!

Cryptograms are messages in substitution code. Break the code to read the quote and its author. For example, THE SMART CAT might become FVO QWGDF JGF if **F** is substituted for **T, V** for **H, O** for **E**, and so on.

"T VEQQN MPRM MPY JYQWEF

VPE MPEAKPM AJ OACRX ORN IY

MPTFXTFK AJ WEOYMPTFK YHWY."

—HTHN MEOHTF

ADDAGRAM

This puzzle functions exactly like an anagram with an added step: In addition to being scrambled, each word below is missing the same letter. Discover the missing letter, then unscramble the words. When you do, you'll reveal a lottery, a type of painting, a thin wire, and a device used to increase the volume of sound.

FERAL   SCORE

AILMENT   IMPERIAL

DROP-A-LETTER

Only 4 of the letters in the top line will make their way through the bottom of this maze and land in the squares below. Once they're there, the letters will spell out this riddle:

What is the name of a cheese that is made backwards?

R O S C H E D U P A I T M

LETTER TILES

Using the letter tiles, create 4 five-letter words. Create 8, and you're a Word Sleuth; create 10, and you're a Word Wonder; create 12, and you're a Word Master!

WORD JIGSAW

Fit the pieces into the frame to form common words reading across and down. There's no need to rotate the pieces; they'll fit as shown, with each piece used once.

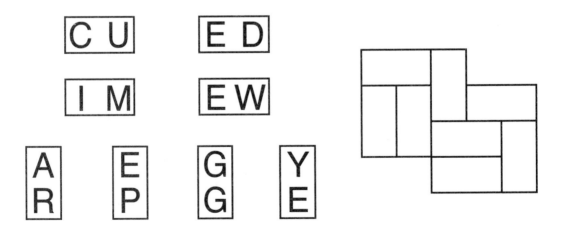

Answers on page 192.

THE FIRST LADY OF CINEMA

Cryptograms are messages in substitution code. Break the code to read the message. For example, THE SMART CAT might become FVO QWGDF JGF if **F** is substituted for **T, V** for **H, O** for **E,** and so on.

"NPL JDUQ MPRC YS MPR NBKJM

NKMP ORUMPRBJ NPRS LYZ EUS

TRDM MPRC YHRB MPR PRUX

NKMP U JDRXWRPUCCRB?"

REWORD REWIND

Unscramble the tiles to form new words that will complete the sentence.

My biggest _____ is not having change for
bus _____.

E A R F

FITTING WORDS (page 5)

RHYME TIME (page 6)

1. bleaker speaker; 2. sad grad;
3. pink drink; 4. frail whale;
5. delay decay; 6. minute fruit;
7. cheery theory; 8. saloon tune

ADDAGRAM (page 7)

The missing letter is **P**.
Leopard, torpedo, dapper, percolate

WORD JIGSAW (page 7)

2 BY 2 (page 8)

1. f) Wuthering Heights
2. i) Rip Van Winkle
3. h) Life with Father
4. c) A Tale of Two Cities
5. g) The Godfather
6. d) Animal Farm
7. b) Sister Carrie
8. j) Robinson Crusoe
9. a) Cannery Row
10. e) The Cat in the Hat

ANALOGIES (page 9)

1. B. wing; 2. A. letter;
3. C. pride; 4. A. cushion

ELEVATOR WORDS (page 10)

1. CASE IN point; 2. point blank;
3. blank space; 4. space station;
5. station break; 6. break dancing;
7. dancing QUEEN

SPLIT DECISIONS (page 11)

Answers may vary.

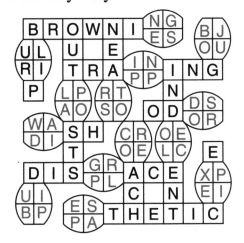

ALPHABET SOUP (page 12)

L I N D A

STRIKE UP THE BAND (page 13)

DRUM, doum, dorm, worm,
worn, HORN

ADDAGRAM (page 13)

The missing letter is I.
Alexis, Madison, Isabella, Elizabeth

ANSWERS

TANGLED WORDS (pages 14-15)

ANSWER THE HOMOPHONE (page 16)

wry, rye

WORD SQUARE (page 16)

S	A	L	T	S
A	W	A	I	T
L	A	R	G	E
T	I	G	E	R
S	T	E	R	N

SWEETNESS (page 17)

spiking/pigskin

WORD JIGSAW (page 17)

CRYPTOKU (page 18)

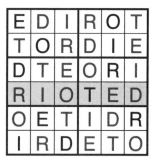

DROP-A-LETTER (page 19)

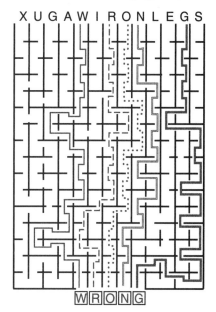

ELEVATOR WORDS (page 20)

1. GREAT Falls; 2. falls back;
3. back country; 4. country code;
5. code word; 6. Word Perfect;
7. Perfect STORM

ANSWERS

FITTING WORDS (page 21)

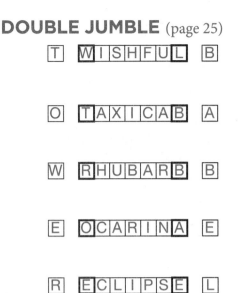

```
C H A F E
H E L I X
E R A S E
F A S T S
```

SPELLEPHONE (page 22)

A. Alabama

B. Florida

C. Georgia

D. Indiana

E. Montana

F. New York

G. Vermont

H. Wyoming

ADDAGRAM (page 23)

The missing letter is **D**.
Orchid, daffodil, dandelion, delphinium

WORD JIGSAW (page 23)

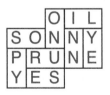

```
    O I L
S O N N Y
P R U N E
Y E S
```

ANAGRAMS FOREVER (page 24)

entirety/eternity

CROSSED WORDS (page 24)

transcendent/immanent

DOUBLE JUMBLE (page 25)

T W I S H F U L B

O T A X I C A B A

W R H U B A R B B

E O C A R I N A E

R E C L I P S E L

RHYME TIME (page 26)

1. monk shrunk; 2. Hubble trouble;
3. levity brevity

RIDDLE IN THE MIDDLE (page 26)

B E G I N

R U L E R

A L O N E

C O V E R

D R E S S

LANGUAGE DETECTIVE (page 27)

The missing word is ESQUIRE.
The second letters of each word
down would then spell EASTER
and the second-to-last letters
PARADE.

ANSWERS

CROSSED WORDS (page 28)
primitive/civilized

NUMBERS IN WORDS (page 28)
1. six

2. eight

3. ten

4. nine

5. two

6. one

ANALOGIES (page 29)
1. B. Hindi; 2. C. pidgin;
3. A. negligent; 4. B. bacteriologist

SPACE SAVERS (page 30)
Look before you leap.
Waste not, want not.

ADD-A-WORD (page 30)
1. rock; 2. dirt; 3. sand; 4. stone;
5. ground; 6. earth

SPLIT DECISIONS (page 31)
Answers may vary.

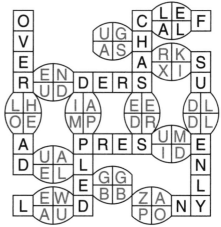

NAME CALLING (page 32)
1. moral; 2. virtue; 3. giraffe;
4. travel; 5. stronger

WORD JIGSAW (page 33)

WORD LADDER (page 33)
DRONE, drove, trove, prove,
prone, PRUNE

CRY, BABY (page 34)
1. Brief Encounter; 2. Old Yeller;
3. Brian's Song; 4. Titanic;
5. Love Story

OPPOSITES (page 34)

FINDING YOU (page 35)
YOUng Yoda found a yo-YO Under YOUr Christmas tree. He tried to use it, but he looked like a monkeY OUt of his tree. After hitting his head, he called his YOUthful friend Yoric and said, "HurrY, OUch!" Yoric rode the TokYO Underground all the way to YOUngstown, whistling the dittY "O Ulysses." "YOU're in luck, Yoda," said Yoric, "I'm a yo-YO User, too." Yoric taught Yoda to yo-yo, and in appreciation Yoda took some candY OUt and gave it to his friend.

ELEVATOR WORDS (page 36)
1. SQUAWK box; 2. box turtle;
3. turtle neck; 4. neck guard;
5. guard rail; 6. rail fence;
7. fence SITTER

ANAGRAM SENTENCES (page 37)
1. lap/pal; 2. dad/add; 3. has/ash;
4. and/Dan; 5. tea/ate

FITTING WORDS (page 38)

```
B A G E L
A N I S E
Y E L P S
S W A Y S
```

ADDAGRAM (page 39)
The missing letter is **C**.
Cancer, Pisces, Scorpio, Capricorn

WORD JIGSAW (page 39)

CHAIN WORDS (page 40)

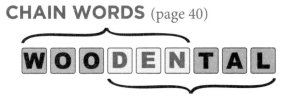

RIDDLE IN THE MIDDLE (page 40)

WASTE

USHER

STOOP

EARLY

TUTOR

ANSWERS

DIY CROSSWORD (page 41)

HONEYCOMB CROSSWORD

(page 42)

CHAIN WORDS (page 43)

RIDDLE (page 43)

Making hay while the sun shines.

WORD COLUMNS (page 44)

Remember that food that has been artfully arranged has had someone else's fingers all over it.

WORD LADDER (page 45)

SISTER, sitter, bitter, bitten, KITTEN

ANAGRAM SENTENCES (page 45)

1. tar/art; 2. any/nay; 3. are/era

ELEVATOR WORDS (page 46)

1. ALMOND paste; 2. paste jewelry;
3. jewelry store; 4. storewide;
5. widescreen; 6. screen name;
7. name DROPPER

WEDGEWORDS (page 47)

SAY WHAT? (page 48)

"I have never met a vampire personally, but I don't know what might happen tomorrow."

WORD TRIANGLE (page 48)

wastewater

SPLIT DECISIONS (page 49)

Answers may vary.

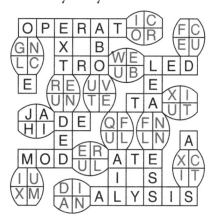

DIY CROSSWORD (page 50)

CHAIN WORDS (page 51)

JUMBLED UP (page 51)

NAME CALLING (page 52)

1. separately; 2. ain't; 3. his home;
4. dimensions

CAST-A-WORD (page 53)

1. A H I M R V

2. B C F P T U

3. D G L O Q S

4. E K N W X Y

ADDAGRAM (page 53)

The missing letter is **S**.
Sapphire, amethyst, moonstone,
turquoise

WORD JIGSAW (page 54)

WORD LADDER (page 54)

BRAIN, drain, drawn, drown,
frown, FLOWN

ANAGRAM SENTENCES (page 55)

1. save/vase; 2. lost/slot; 3. odor/door;
4. pare/pear; 5. goat/toga

OPPOSITES (page 55)

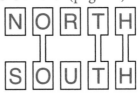

MINI-CROSS (page 56)

LETTER TILES (page 57)

1. range; 2. reign; 3. raise; 4. siren;
5. snore. (Other possible solutions:
snare; organ; noise; groan; grain;
anger; inner; arise; gears.)

SAY WHAT? (page 57)

"I went to a fight the other night and
a hockey game broke out."

ANSWERS

WORD COLUMNS (page 58)

I watch television with my neighbors next door. They have a big screen TV and I have a pair of binoculars.

WEDGEWORDS (page 59)

CHAIN WORDS (page 60)

S E L D O M I N O

OPPOSITES (page 60)

T A R D Y

E A R L Y

ADDAGRAM (page 61)

The missing letter is **E**.
Antique, tureen, policeman, overdue

WORD JIGSAW (page 61)

WORD LADDER (page 62)

Answers may vary.
BIGOT, begot, begat, began, vegan, VEGAS

ANAGRAM SENTENCES (page 62)

1. aunt/tuna; 2. pots/tops; 3. snap/pans

DROP-A-LETTER (page 63)

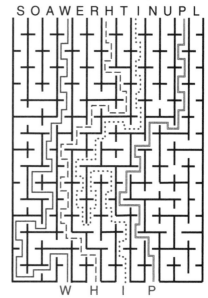

ABOUT TIME (pages 64-65)

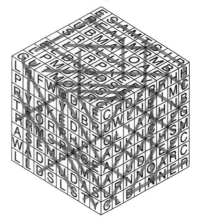

ANSWERS

DIY CROSSWORD (page 66)

FITTING WORDS (page 67)

S	A	M	B	A
O	B	O	E	S
F	L	A	S	K
T	E	N	T	S

ELEVATOR WORDS (page 68)

1. GET IN touch; 2. touchstone; 3. stone-cold; 4. cold feet; 5. Feet First; 6. first ladies; 7. ladies NIGHT

CHAIN WORDS (page 69)

OPPOSITES (page 69)

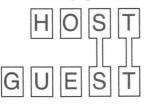

ANAGRAM SENTENCES (page 70)

1. astute/statue; 2. allure/laurel; 3. skater/streak; 4. recall/cellar

LETTER TILES (page 70)

1. lime; 2. tame; 3. lean; 4. late; 5. mean; 6. tent; 7. tilt; 8. melt; 9. mint; 10. mile. (Other possible solutions: malt; lent; nail; tail; tile.)

CAST-A-WORD (page 71)

1. A L P S V W

2. B C I Q R T

3. D E G K M Y

4. F H J N O U

ADDAGRAM (page 71)

The missing letter is **Y**.
Syringe, scythe, olympiad, abysmal

WORD JIGSAW (page 72)

WORD LADDER (page 72)

LOAN, loaf, leaf, lean, bean, beat, PEAT

CAN'T SEE THE TREES FOR THE FOREST? (page 73)

1. pine; 2. yew; 3. cedar; 4. elm; 5. ash; 6. teak; 7. fir; 8. larch

ANSWERS

MOVIE GENRES (pages 74-75)

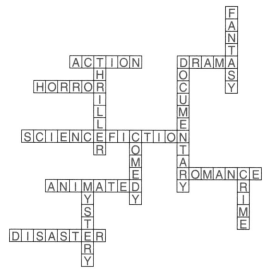

DIY CROSSWORD (page 78)

ANAGRAM SENTENCES (page 76)

1. present/serpent; 2. senator/treason;
3. gallery/allergy; 4. married/admirer

OPPOSITES (page 76)

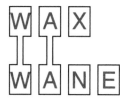

CAST-A-WORD (page 77)

1. A H K L R Z

2. B C F O S W

3. D I M T U V

4. E G J N P Y

ADDAGRAM (page 77)

The missing letter is **L**.
Trifle, strudel, apple crisp, banana split

QUOTE ME! (page 79)

"All that is valuable in human society depends upon the opportunity for development accorded the individual."

WORD TRIANGLE (page 79)

ASCENDANCE

DOUBLE JUMBLE (page 80)

L NEWSMAN S

E ENVIOUS E

N NECKTIE A

T ENDLESS S

E TAFFETA O

N LUMBAGO N

WORD LADDER (page 81)
CRUMPET, trumpet, trumped, thumped, THUMBED

ANAGRAM (page 81)
D. San Diego, Tucson, Las Vegas

WORD COLUMNS (page 82)
"I don't want to achieve immortality through my work; I want to achieve immortality through not dying."

ADDAGRAM (page 83)
The missing letter is **F**.
Flipper, caffeine, foreign, flimsy

WORD JIGSAW (page 83)

ELEVATOR WORDS (page 84)
1. GREEN salad; 2. salad bar;
3. barfly; 4. fly high; 5. high-rolling;
6. rolling pin; 7. pin CUSHION

HONEYCOMB CROSSWORD
(page 85)

VEGETABLE TOGS (page 86)

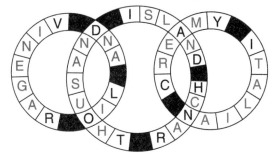

SAY WHAT? (page 87)
"Do not go where the path may lead, go instead where there is no path and leave a trail."

WORD TRIANGLE (page 87)
THREATENER

ANAGRAM (page 88)
Blueberry, pear, apricot

CHAIN WORDS (page 88)

WORD LADDER (page 89)
SMILE, smite, spite, spire, shire, shirt, short, shore, CHORE

ANSWERS

DOUBLE JUMBLE (page 90)

C **CHRONIC** P

H **RAVIOLI** I

U **HIBACHI** C

R **HARDTOP** N

C **UNKNOWN** I

H **CLASSIC** C

ANAGRAM CROSSWORD (page 91)

CAST-A-WORD (page 92)

. A C S W Y Z

. B F I L O P

. D E H K M T

. J N R U V X

QUOTE ME! (page 92)

"A coward is much more exposed to quarrels than a man of spirit."

SPLIT DECISIONS (page 93)

Answers may vary.

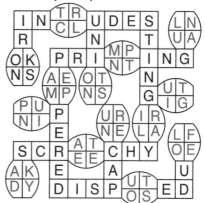

WORD JIGSAW (page 94)

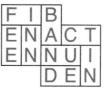

CITIES AND STATES (page 94)

Fargo; Indiana; Maine; Salem; Seattle; Texas

A DARK KNIGHT (page 95)

HEATH, heats, hefts, hafts, harts, parts, pares, pores, pokes, jokes, JOKER

ANSWERS

TANGLED WORDS (pages 96-97)

THE STAR-SPANGLED BANNER (page 98)

60

ADD-A-LETTER (page 99)

TACO

HERO

MELT

WRAP

FRIES

CAESAR

YOGURT

CAST-A-WORD (page 100)

1. A D G J N Q
2. C F L O T U
3. E M P S X Z
4. H I K R W Y

ADDAGRAM (page 100)

The missing letter is **G**.
Grenade, allergy, midget, and longitude

WORD JIGSAW (page 101)

OPPOSITES (page 101)

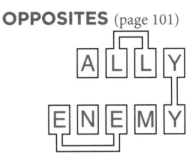

THE PRINCESS OF MONACO (page 102)

GRACE, grade, grads, brads, beads, heads, heals, seals, sells, bells, belly, KELLY

ELEVATOR WORDS (page 103)

1. MOTHER goose; 2. goose egg;
3. egg cream; 4. cream sauce;
5. saucepan; 6. pancake; 7. cake MIX

STEPWORDS (page 104)

SWIMSUIT

ALPHABET SOUP (page 105)

JOYCE

ANSWERS

WORD JIGSAW (page 106)

```
I M P
R E E F S
K N E E L
    K E Y
```

ADDAGRAM (page 106)

The missing letter is **C**.

Crimson, monarchy, chronicle, nuclear

HONEYCOMB CROSSWORD (page 107)

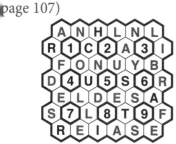

```
A N H L N L
R 1 C 2 A 3 I
F O N U Y B
D 4 U 5 S 6 R
E L D E S A
S 7 L 8 T 9 F
R E I A S E
```

MIND STRETCHER (page 108)

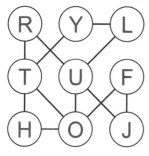

R Y L
T U F
H O J

WORD TRIO (page 108)

```
M O R N I N G
  N O
& N I G H T
```

WORD JIGSAW (page 109)

```
    T H E
S P O I L
K I O S K
I N K
```

CHAIN WORDS (page 109)

R E C E N T I T Y

"HI-YO, SILVER, AWAY!" (page 110)

RANGER, ringer, linger, longer, lodger, Dodger, dodder, fodder, folder, solder, solver, SILVER

CODEWORD (page 111)

```
1  2  3  4  5  6  7  8  9  10 11 12 13
G  L  C  A  S  Y  Z  M  V  D  R  U  J
```

```
14 15 16 17 18 19 20 21 22 23 24 25 26
H  W  T  Q  B  O  F  E  X  P  N  K  I
```

185

ANSWERS

STEPWORDS (page 112)
ROCKETS

6. SS
5. CAP
4. FUSE
3. BLAZE
2. MORTAR
1. SPARKLE

BREEZY NEWS (page 113)
When one door shuts, another opens—which means you live in a drafty house.

MIND STRETCHER (page 113)

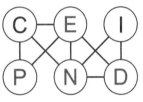

C — E — I
P — N — D

DOUBLED UP (pages 114-115)
The 10-letter word is: Particular

PASTRAMI
RI   EX
IM   DECANTER
PLEASANT   TI
IC   TU   DIAGONAL
IT   RA   PL   TI
ANTEROOM   TU
          ATTITUDE

WORD LADDER (page 116)
Answers may vary.
BLOCK, black, slack, stack, stark, START

DECORATIVE WORD (page 116)
ornamentation

WEDGEWORDS (page 117)

P E S T
R I T E
I D E A
D E E R
E R R S

DIS CON NEC TED (page 118)
2. mer; 3. co; 4. sm; 5. merci;
6. Ali; 7. com
Mystery word: commercialism

CAST-A-WORD (page 119)
1. A L P S V W
2. B F I T Y Z
3. C D J M N U
4. E G H K O R

ADDAGRAM (page 119)
The missing letter is **E**.
Magazine, recipe, emulate, permeable

WORD JIGSAW (page 120)

A M P
D E L T A
S T O O P
    T O T

GAME CHANGE (page 120)
Exchange G and M to get MAGE.

M A G E

ANSWERS

WORD LADDER (page 121)
BASE, bass, bats, hats, HITS

LETTER TILES (page 121)
1. noise; 2. niece; 3. niche; 4. snoop;
5. crime. (Other possible solutions:
sheer; nicer; scene; sheen; prime; preen.)

AFRICA (pages 122-123)

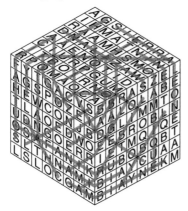

ELEVATOR WORDS (page 124)
1. WATERED-silk; 2. silk cotton;
3. cotton candy; 4. candy apple;
5. apple butter; 6. butter dish;
7. dish RACK

ACTORS SCRAMBLEGRAM (page 125)

DEAR DIARY (page 126)
"I never travel without my diary.
One should always have something
sensational to read." — Oscar Wilde

JUMBLED UP (page 126)

GRID FILL (page 127)

STILL A HERO (page 128)
Answers may vary.
FORD, fore, sore, sole, SOLO

REWORD REWIND (page 128)
rats/star

NOT QUITE A CROSSWORD SNACK (page 129)
The hidden word is "Easter."

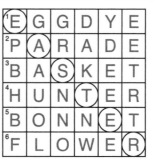

ANSWERS

HOCKEY TEAMS (page 130)

CAST-A-WORD (page 131)

1. A H L N R T
2. B E J K M Y
3. C F I U W Z
4. D O P Q S V

WORD JIGSAW (page 131)

MISSING CONNECTIONS (page 132)

WORD COLUMNS (page 133)

"True happiness is the full use of your powers along lines of excellence in a life affording scope."

FITTING WORDS (page 134)

ADDAGRAM (page 135)

The missing letter is **Y**.
Strategy, synapse, maternity, worthy

WORD JIGSAW (page 135)

QUIRKS OF THE CHAMPS
(page 136)

Whenever he played in a match, tennis champ Jimmy Connors kept a note from his grandmother tucked into his sock for luck.

WORD LADDER (page 136)

GOLD, goad, load, lead, LEAF

ANSWERS

WEDGEWORDS (page 137)

```
C A R T
A M I R
B I T E
I D E A
N E S T
```

DOUBLED UP (pages 138-139)

The 10-letter word is: Irrelevant

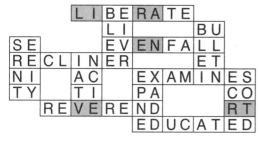

```
      L I B E R A T E
          L I       B U
        E V E N F A L L
S E     R E C L I N E R   E T
R E C L I N E R
N I   A C     E X A M I N E S
T Y   T I     P A       C O
  R E V E R E N D         R T
          E D U C A T E D
```

A TO Z (page 140)

```
Y Z
X M L
N W K
O V H J A
P U I G B
Q S T F C
  R E D
```

PROFESSIONAL SCRAMBLEGRAM (page 141)

```
G L O R I O U S T E N
N E U R O L O G I S T
T             E N
R             L I
E             E C
E             C E
P             T A
R             R R
I             I T
N             C I
E             I C
T             A L
E             N E
R
  I L L U S T R A T O R
  U T R I L L O S T A R
```

```
N S E T C I I S T
S C I E N T I S T
```

WORD COLUMNS (page 142)

The best way to set a new record is to be far away from any tape measures, scales, or witnesses.

MISSING CONNECTIONS (page 143)

```
F I R E W O R K S
L E     A     T
A D D S   S T A R S
G     W   E     I
    S   H   O P T
B U N T I N G   E
L   I   T   A D S
A P P L E   B   J
N     A   B L U E
D I S P L A Y   T
```

FITTING WORDS (page 144)

```
J E W E L
O X I D E
B I N G E
S T E E R
```

ANSWERS

ALPHABET SOUP (page 145)

B R I A N

TOP SPIN (page 146)

1. A F N P T
2. B C E H M
3. D K Q R X
4. G I J S W
5. L O U V Z

ADDAGRAM (page 146)

The missing letter is **D**.
Tragedy, watershed, dragon, mandolin

WORD JIGSAW (page 147)

YOU HEARD IT HERE FIRST!

(page 147)

If it is not a boy it will be a girl, says the fortune-teller. —Madagascar proverb

ANALOGIES (page 148)

1. C. breeze; 2. B. sneeze; 3. C. yank;
4. A. web

A TO Z (page 149)

CODEWORD (page 150)

BUNNY ZIGZAG (page 151)

REWORD REWIND (page 151)

shop/hops

VISUALIZE THIS! (page 152)

Beans, cabbages, rhubarb, spinach, carrots, beetroot, mange tout, peas, tomatoes, leeks, brussels sprouts.

ADDAGRAM (page 153)

The missing letter is **Z**.
Tweezers, bronze, gazelle, citizen

WORD JIGSAW (page 153)

ANSWERS

CROSSED WORDS (page 154)
common/denominator

GOOD EATS UP NORTH (page 154)
Poutine, a popular comfort food in Canada, is French fries topped with fresh cheese curds, then covered with brown gravy.

FITTING WORDS (page 155)

I	R	A	T	E
M	O	C	H	A
P	U	R	E	R
S	T	E	E	L

SPLIT DECISIONS (page 156)
Answers may vary.

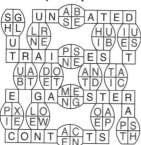

ELEVATOR WORDS (page 157)
1. DIAMONDback; 2. backwater;
3. water table; 4. table wine;
5. wine cooler; 6. cooler weather;
7. weather THE STORM

MISSING CONNECTIONS
(page 158)

RHYME TIME (page 159)
1. strange change; 2. shark park;
3. elite street; 4. fake ache;
5. maroon balloon; 6. grill skill;
7. prize pies; 8. choose views

DOUBLED UP (pages 160-161)
The 10-letter word is: Cartoonist

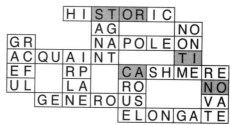

GREEDY SCRAMBLEGRAM (page 162)

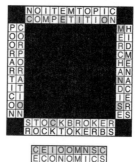

CAST-A-WORD (page 163)
1. A B D F J W
2. C N O P S Y
3. E K L M U X
4. G H I R T V

WORD JIGSAW (page 163)

ODD ONE OUT (page 164)

DAVID. All the other words are palindromes.

ABC (page 164)

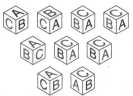

CAST-A-WORD (page 165)

1. A C H J N O
2. B F I Q T Y
3. D E G K S X
4. L P R U V W

ADDAGRAM (page 165)

The missing letter is **U**.
Ritual, nucleus, lucrative, altruism

FITTING WORDS (page 166)

ANALOGIES (page 167)

1. C. Topeka; 2. B. pitcher;
3. C. cat; 4. A. sailboat

OH, NO-O-O-O! (page 168)

"I worry that the person who thought up Muzak may be thinking up something else." —Lily Tomlin

ADDAGRAM (page 168)

The mystery letter is **F**.
Raffle, fresco, filament, amplifier

DROP A LETTER (page 169)

LETTER TILES (page 170)

Answers may vary. 1. clods; 2. cloud;
3. clued; 4. colds; 5. could; 6. disco;
7. duels; 8. idles; 9. locus; 10. slice

WORD JIGSAW (page 170)

THE FIRST LADY OF CINEMA

(page 171)
"Why slap them on the wrist with feathers when you can belt them over the head with a sledgehammer?"
—Katharine Hepburn

REWORD REWIND (page 171)

fear/fare